Labyrinth Fish — The Bubble-Nest-Builders

Horst Linke

® 1991 Tetra-Press
Tetra Werke Dr. rer nat. Ulrich Baensch GmbH
P.O. Box 15 80, D-4520 Melle, Germany

1st edition 1 — 10.000, 1992
Typesetting: Fotosatz Hoffmann, Hennef
Printed in Germany

Distributed in U.S.A. by
Tetra Sales (Division of Warner-Lambert)
Morris Plains, N.J. 07950
Distributed in UK by Tetra Sales, Lambert Court,
Chestnut Avenue, Eastleigh Hampshire 505 3ZQ
WL-Code: 16071

ISBN 3-89356-137-4

Horst Linke

LABYRINTH FISH
THE BUBBLE-NEST-BUILDERS

Their identification, care and breeding

FOREWORD

The revision of the genus Betta proposed by RICHTER (1981 + 1982), splitting it into Betta, Pseudobetta and Parophiocephalus is not taken into consideration in this book. The author is not following the suggested revision because it has not been possible to observe all the species in this genus. As the critically important factor of reproductive biology of some of the species available only as preserved specimens has been based on speculation, it is felt it is not yet feasible to classify on the basis of the new genera.

I should like to thank the following for their kind help and support: Dr. Sylvia BERNS, Dr. W. FOERSCH, Dr. W. LADIGES, Dr. Hans M. PETERS, J. GECK, T. SCHULZ, D. SCHALLER, Ms. J. BAER, N. NEUGEBAUER and Dr. R. Digdo YUWONO − Dr. Liem-Vivaria INDONESIA.

I should also like to express my thanks to my esteemed club associate Otto SCHULZ, to Klaus DERWANZ in Bangkok and to the manager of the Star Aquarium in Bangkok, Mister KREE Thamongkol, as well as my friends in the FITOBE who accompanied me on many trips.

Special thanks are due to Father Heinz Stroh MSF for his very constructive and wide ranging comments on numerous biotopes in Kalimantan.

Last but not least, many thanks to the Tetra Publishing Division whose generous cooperation has enabled this volume to appear in colours that do justice to the subject matter.

Schwarzenbach am Wald
August 1992   Horst Linke

CONTENTS

THE AFRICAN LABYRINTH FISH

THE LABYRINTH FISH

Labyrinth fish can certainly be considered amongst the most interesting and colourful of all ornamental fish. They are generally undemanding subjects and few of them have any special requirements in respect of their care. In the wild they are subtropical and tropical freshwater fish. Their natural distribution is restricted to Africa and Asia. These fish display some strikingly interesting behavioural patterns with the males of some species so aggressive that it is not unusual for encounters between two of them to turn into life or death battles.

For more than a century fights between "Pla-Kat", literally "biting and tearing fish", have been arranged in Thailand as a form of sport and betting medium. The species involved are wild forms of the Siamese fighting fish, *Betta splendens* and *Betta smaragdina*.

For breeding, many labyrinth fish build rather sophisticated nests of air bubbles, often reinforced with plant material, that may float on the surface or be concealed in underwater cavities. The fish then spawn under these, an act that involves much intertwining and writhing of bodies. Although there are various species that dispense with the nest building, all species indulge in a remarkable courtship display by the males. A high proportion of them practise brood care, with the male defending the nest

Betta splendens
The typical writhing courtship display of spawning labyrinth fish.

The labyrinth respiratory organ of *Anabas testudineus* with the gill cover removed.

Magnified section.

Fighting fish (wild form) on the Sunday market in Bangkok.

Young Thailanders from Bangkok, keen spectators at a fish fight.

and the growing fry with the utmost devotion.

In the Ceylon Macropodus species, *Belontia signata,* this brood care extends to both parents who look after their offspring for weeks on end.

There are also various labyrinth fish that "brood" their young in their mouth. Some species emit crackling noises during courtship displays or disputes. There is also another species that puckers its lips, so that the parties involved seem to be kissing.

Some species are even capable of leaving the water and migrating overland to other habitats. The labyrinth fish also include a number of "jumpers" that catch their prey with a smart leap from the water or shoot down insects by "spitting" a jet of water from their mouths. For this reason any aquarium containing these species must be well covered or have a blanket of floating plants screening the surface of the water.

The vast majority of labyrinth fish need warm conditions. As they take in atmospheric air at the surface, this also needs to be fairly warm. Within the labyrinth fish family there are some astonishing differences in size. For instance, the smallest species is only three centimeters long when fully grown whilst the largest grows to 70 cm.

Labyrinth fish are not merely ornamental species but also have commercial import-

ance with the larger ones being raised as a valuable source of food on fish farms in different parts of Asia. Fed on a diet of pig manure, they can grow to a very impressive size in some of the extensive open air fishponds. Since the high temperatures that prevail here make dead fish a very perishable commodity, the capacity of these "air breathing" fish to survive for quite lengthy periods in humid conditions makes them a valuable asset. What is more, they are a tasty morsel in their own right. The giant gourami, *Osphronemus goramy,* which weighs in at up to 7 kilograms, has a very delicate flavour. The same is true of the kissing gourami, *Helostoma temminckii,* which, although only growing to 1 kg, is commonly on sale on Asian markets.

However, it would also be true to describe the Siamese fighting fish, *Betta splendens,* as a "commercial" fish because, raised by the hundreds of thousands by many Thai families, it represents the "product" upon which they depend for their livelihood. The species is not only popular amongst Asians but is also in great demand on the export market.

So what is meant by this collective term "labyrinth fish"? Essentially, they all possess a supplementary respiratory organ, the so-called labyrinth, that enables them to take in atmospheric air which they obtain from the

9

surface of the water. If they were prevented from doing so, the majority of these species would suffocate in their natural environment, water. Only a few species are equipped with sufficiently developed gills to enable them to obtain the oxygen they require in the conventional way. Once the air is gulped in, it is forced back through the mouth cavity into the labyrinth, an extension of the gill cavity located above the gill arches. In this cavity, which is found on both sides of the head, there are countless very thin, skin-covered plates (lamellae), seemingly arranged in a random, hence labyrinthine, fashion. The highly vascularized nature of this skin cover enables the oxygen to be extracted from the air and passed into the bloodstream. This respiratory structure allows the fish to inhabit stretches of rather inhospitable water — low in oxygen and with uncomfortably high temperatures — that might otherwise be classed as foetid puddles. The oxygen content of the water is often so low that it is only thanks to labyrinth respiration that the fish manage to keep alive and struggle through to the next rainy season. The more demanding species are generally those that come from flowing jungle streams and rivers where the oxygen levels are higher. These are usually capable of balancing their oxygen requirements via their gills.

Systematically, the labyrinth fish belong to the sub order *Anabantoidei* in the order of the *Perciformes*, percoids. They comprise four families and three sub families which in turn are divided into genera.

1. Family: Anabantidae

with the genera: *Anabas, Ctenopoma*

2. Family: Belontiidae

Sub Family: *Belontiinae*

with the genus: *Belontia*

Sub Family: *Macropodinae*

with the genera: *Betta, Macropodus, Malpulutta, Parosphromenus, Pseudosphromenus, Trichopsis*

Sub Family: *Trichogasterinae*

with the genera: *Colisa, Ctenops, Parasphaerichthys, Sphaerichthys, Trichogaster*

3. Family: Helostomatidae

with the genus: *Helostoma*

4. Family: Osphronemidae

with the genus: *Osphronemus*

These four families cover the labyrinth fish in the true sense of the word which is what this book will deal with exclusively.

The snake-head fish *(Channa)* and shark-heads *(Luciocephalus)*, which are only distant cousins of the labyrinth fish in terms of lifestyle and physical attributes, are not considered here.

At this point it is perhaps appropriate to mention another facet of taxonomy, namely the extent to which amateur fish keepers can get annoyed over the convoluted scientific names of the creatures in their care. So there is a distinct and natural preference for the vernacular terms which are, however, often so variable as to be the subject of controversy between hobbyists in neighbouring towns who cannot agree on a name for one and the same fish. This sort of local disagreement makes the likelihood of a consensus at even a national level somewhat faint. The Swedish botanist, Carl von LINNE (LINNAEUS), established a unified, scientific identification system for the animal kingdom to overcome this problem in 1758 and this still serves as the basis for the present day binomial nomenclature. Binomial nomenclature entails allocating a dual name for effective scientific classification. For instance, if an amateur wants to look up information about the spotted climbing perch, this lay term could lead to confusion under certain circumstances. However, if you use the term *Ctenopoma acutirostre*, all adherents to the fish keeping hobby will know which fish is meant. But the scientific term can tell you still more. If we stick with the same example and write the name in full, we will come up with *Ctenopoma acutirostre* (PELLEGRIN, 1899). The first name *"Ctenopoma"* indicates the genus and is written with a capital letter. It enables us to recognise the type of fish we are dealing with, provided we can classify it to a family. The second name, *"acutirostre"*, indicates the species and is always written with a small letter. This name is accorded "priority" in the sense that if the generic name is ever altered, the fish will retain its specific name in any event, in precisely the way that its original classifier had described it. Since both items, that is the generic and specific names, must be in Latin or at least Latinised, and since the specific name must have the same grammatical gender as the generic name, then only the last syllables of the specific name may be altered in the event of the genus being renamed. The third name (PELLEGRIN, 1899) with the year, tells us that the French ichthyologist first decribed this fish in 1899 as *Anabas acutirostre*. If one finds a second specific name in addition to the first — like, for example, the Asiatic labyrinth fish *Macropodus opercularis concolor* (AHL, 1936) — one can tell that the fish in question is a sub species, namely "concolor".

Macropodus opercularis concolor is therefore a sub species of *Macropodus opercularis* and belongs to the genus *Macropodus*, it was first described by Dr. Ernst AHL in 1936. These remarks on the correct naming of our fish may appear somewhat complicated at first glance but they do illustrate how they eliminate ambiguity and that non standard vernacular terms can only play a secondary role in any system of nomenclature.

Finally, some attention should be paid to the identification and description of the external characteristics of labyrinth fish. Generally speaking, the head relates to the tip of the snout to the rear end of the gill cover or gill cleft. From here on, as far as the top of the anus, is termed the rump. The remaining part as far as the root of the tail, i.e. the point where the caudal fin starts, is called the tail. The caudal peduncle ends at the same point but commences at the rear end of the anal fin. Labyrinth fish have a dorsal fin on their back and a pectoral fin on either side of their front end. Beneath the body, usually at the same level as the pectoral fins are two often elongated ventral fins forming thread-like extensions in many species. At the lower end of the body is the anal fin. At this end of the body is the caudal peduncle which bears the caudal fin.

Arising from this are the following scientific measurements: total or overall length, often given only as the length, is taken as indicating the length from the tip of the snout to the tip of the tail.

After these brief introductory remarks we can now get on with a presentation of the various species in question. This will be done in alphabetical order, taking no account of families, sub families or the species contained therein with the aim of providing a description of each species with as much detail as possible and backed up by a colour photograph. Species for which no colour photograph could be found have been left out of this work on the grounds that the species concerned are for the most part very rare and have not been imported live in most cases. I hope that these omissions will not be considered too grave.

In the course of my frequent trips to Africa and Asia I have managed to catch and bring back a number of rare species myself so that I am able to describe and illustrate these in a book for the first time.

The objective of this volume is to provide a comprehensive study of labyrinth fish together with their natural habitat, details of their requirements in captivity with notes on optimum breeding conditions. In principle, one would have liked to have avoided pointless repetition but as the book is intended as a reference work, reiteration of some material proved inevitable where species have identical behaviour and distribution ranges.

THE MODERN AQUARIUM FOR LABYRINTH FISH

Technical parameters:

In my presentation of the different species I shall frequently refer to a variety of possible items of aquarium equipment that relate specifically to the individual species in question or to groups of species whose requirements and behaviour are similar.

So that you, the reader, will have an idea of the basic technical parameters required for keeping labyrinth fish, I will start by giving an outline description of a large and smaller aquarium suitable for these subjects.

When setting up and equipping the "large" aquarium it is essential that the following prerequisites should be borne in mind: The first thing to consider is its support — where it is going to stand. There is a wide range of ready made cabinets available, in a variety of wood finishes to suit the decor of your room. If you decide to build the stand yourself, take care to ensure that it is stable and that the floor is capable of withstanding the loading. An aquarium measuring 130 cm long, by 40 cm wide and 50 cm deep, including acces-

Colisa labiosa

sories, weighs around 6 hundredweight (!), excluding the stand. Clearly, you are going to need a stable floor.

You are also going to want a decent view of the aquarium and for this you will want to position it at normal eye level when seated. Check that your stand is true with a spirit level because any oversight will later be reflected in a discrepancy between the water level and the rim of the tank. In addition, the stand must offer a clean, even surface for the aquarium to rest on, so as to exclude the chance of any untoward stresses arising. A thin polystyrene sheet, cut to the size of the tank, should be positioned under the aquarium to take some of the weight. As polystyrene is readily deformed under load, it is advisable to cut out 4 or 5 rectangular patches, 200 x 150 mm in size, from the middle so as to prevent crimpling of the material. If you decide to go for the most up to date and reliable form of heating, Tetra Plan, a flexible, electrically heated mat, then this should be placed on the polystyrene sheet. For it to sit well it should be switched on for a few minutes until it is warm to the touch. The heating mat should be about the same size as the base of the aquarium. An appropriate section should also be cut from the polystyrene sheet to accommodate the connector plate of the heating mat. The aquarium can now be positioned on to the stand and heating mat. In each case the actual size will be determined by the circumstances of the particular aquarium owner. The bigger the aquarium, the greater will be the volume of water thus rendering the task of maintaining stable water quality easier.

Natural lighting of the aquarium cannot be favoured because of the uneven and changeable light values. Preference should always (!) be given to artificial lighting. If the aquarium is a free standing unit offering a view from above into this aquatic world, the best form of heating is attractive mercury vapour lamps suspended over the tank from above. If you decide to light your tank with fluorescent tubes you should take the length of these into account when selecting your aquarium. 20 Watt fluorescent tubes are 59 cm long, about 65 cm including fix-

ings and thus are suitable for a 70 cm aquarium. 40 Watt fluorescent tubes are 120 cm long, about 126 cm including fixings — ideal for a 130 cm aquarium. Similarly, for a 170 cm aquarium the appropriate heating medium would be 65 Watt tubes at 150 cm or 166 cm including fixings.

Every aquarium should have a back wall. This gives the fish a greater sense of security and enhances the overall impression of a nicely decorated aquarium. The attraction of an underwater landscape is much reduced if the floral print of your wallpaper is intruding from behind. There are a number of possible solutions. For instance, dealers stock a wide range of backdrops in the form of photographic prints that can be stuck on to the outside of the rear pane of glass. A dark coloured decorative panel is also a possibility. But for me the ideal type of backdrop always was and still is an irregular structure incorporating a number of cavities and hideaways and forming part of the underwater world itself. This kind of structure has been the subject of various experiments. They have been made in cement, wood, cork and many other similar materials. The simplest and cheapest method, though unfortunately something of a rarity in the range of the average pet shop, is made from polystyrene, It is easy to work with even if you are not blessed with a talent for handicraft.

I should like to give a brief description of the technique used for making these "props". First buy some polystyrene plates generally available in 50 x 100 cm sheets with thicknesses from 10 mm upwards. For our back wall we take 50 mm thick plates. The most suitable tool for working with this material is a soldering iron with an 80 Watt rating. The copper tip of the soldering iron should be filed down so that the tip is knife-shaped. This hot soldering iron will cut through the hard polystyrene foam like butter. The straight tip is used to cut the sheets to size and then one decides which side to use as front or back. The edges of the back side are chamfered so that they will fit into the aquarium better and do not cause the inside edge to protrude. If two sheets have to be fitted next to each other to form the back wall in a case where the length of the tank is over one metre, the sheets should be cut in such a way that they form equal sections under the crosspiece that often bridges the middle of a tank. The tightest possible fit is very important for the polystyrene sections of the back wall because the natural buoyancy of this material tends to make it want to float upwards.

In order to impart the required sculpted shape to the backdrop you should now take a pair of pliers and bend the tip of the soldering iron into a hook shape which can be used to carve out scoops and curves of varying sizes in the foam material. With a bit of imagination there is no limit to what can be achieved. A selection of caves and hollows, filled with sand and planted up with suitable vegetation will work wonders for the overall visual effect. The thickness of the material allows plenty of scope.

Once the basic backdrop is completed, it may still have something of a rough edged appearance. To smooth things off the polystyrene sheet can be held over a burning candle or a cigarette lighter (medium flame) until the heat has softened and rounded off the edges. At thisk point the structure itself can be regarded as finished and ready for painting. For this one should use undiluted dispersion colours that are available from any paint shop for toning down topcoats. Dark colours such as browns, dark greys or black, are recommended but here again you are free to "mix'n' match" to suit your individual taste. The paint is applied undiluted with a brush, covering all sides, including the back. But do be careful, because these paints are very difficult to clean off any items of clothing once they have dried, if not impossible! Before they dry they are water soluble and any spots can be readily cleaned from any surface. Once painted, the backdrop should be left to dry for two to three days at normal temperatures. At this point any retouching work can be carried out before leaving to dry for the same length of time again. Before the piece is finally put into the aquarium, it should be "presoaked" for a few hours. For this treatment it is placed in a

water-filled container such as a bathtub and then rinsed off under fresh running water. Polystyrene backdrops made in this way will last for years and have been successfully tried and tested in marine and freshwater aquaria.

The backdrop is then positioned in the aquarium, making sure that it fits tight and snug. It is now time to lay the aquarium bed. The recommended ground cover material is fine, dark gravel with a grain size of 1 to 3 mm. I am not an advocate of those types with a larger diameter, the so-called pea gravels, as they tend to harbour dirt. I have never come across a biotope in either Africa or Asia where the bed was made up of coarse gravel. Provided that this fine gravel does not contain any obvious visible impurities, it can be put into the tank unwashed to form a layer up to 1 cm deep. If it contains a small proportion of loam this might prove beneficial to plant growth.

If you have not opted for the heating mat as your source of heat, this is the point at which you should provide a cable heater as your heating element in the aquarium. For this the cable heater is switched on for a short time until it is warm to the touch and it should then be laid in a spiral on the previously smoothed gravel bed. The amount of heating needed can be calculated on the basis of approximately 0.2 to 0.3 Watts per liter of water. At this stage a further 1 cm deep layer of gravel is spread over the tank bed covering the cable heater. In order to provide the plants with a stimulating growing medium we then put in a thin layer of the latest kind of nutrient stabiliser, containing iron and other organic substances. This medium, such as Tetra Initial D which is specially formulated to simulate tropical soil beds is mixed with a little more gravel and spread over the whole of the tank bottom. Finally, a further, thoroughly washed 3 to 4 cm deep layer of gravel should be applied with a slight gradient rising towards the back wall.

After this, any items of decoration, like roots of bogwood and rocks should be put into position. Take care to ensure that the rocks are lime-free, a simple test being to apply a few drops of hydrochloric acid to the stone. If the surface starts to foam up and dissolve on contact with the acid the stones are calcareous and so not suitable for the aquarium. The decorative pieces should be firmly bedded into the gravel. And if you intend to keep any digging fish, such as the dwarf cichlids, then you should set the pieces right on the bottom plate. The "earth moving" activities of these fish have been known to undermine rocks to the extent that these have collapsed totally, killing fish and even breaking panes of glass.

Other items of decoration that may be used, apart from bogwood and stones, include carefully cleaned coconut shells with a small opening cut into them and strategically positioned to add to the attraction of the underwater landscape.

Once all the decorative elements have been concluded, including the building of little cliffs and cavities, the water can be put into the tank. So as not to disturb your careful preparatory work, cover the entire surface of the sand with paper and place on it a shallow dish or other container. Carefully pour the water into this until the aquarium is half full. Unfortunately, you are almost certainly going to have to use tap water for this task and it can hardly be classed as ideal. The substance we usually obtain from the mains supply is either hard or medium hard water, often "enriched" with other minerals. Accordingly, the hydrogen ion concentration (pH value) of this water often lies in the basic i. e. alkaline range which is to say a type of water that our fish are most unlikely to encounter in their natural habitats.

For this reason, anyone who intends to keep fish should obtain a full picture of the water values of his tap water by carrying out his own tests. Tetra have developed a range of reasonably priced, uncomplicated, water testing indicators that react in a matter of seconds to give you instant readings for the general hardness, carbonate hardness, nitrite content and pH value of your water. If you have a ready source of rainwater available, you will be able to mix this with your tap water to give a product that is closer to natural water. However, it is worth pointing out that pure rain water or very soft water with a low mineral content is often too un-

stable for normal fish keeping requirements though it is ideal for breeding and raising fry. In my experience the best values for normal fish keeping conditions are general and carbonate hardness levels between 5 and 7° dH with a pH value that is stable around the 6.5 to 6.7 mark.

Once half of the water has been let into the tank you can make a start on planting. For the back of the aquarium tall, stemmed plants should be selected. These should be set out in sizeable groups, densely planted in little circles at 1 to 2 cm apart. A sparsely planted aquarium turns out to be a false economy because it is those tanks that are well stocked with greenery that ultimately have the most visual appeal. Moreover, they offer fish much appreciated opportunities to hide themselves away. What is more, aquatic plants fulfill an important and wide ranging biological role in maintaining water quality and for this reason at least 20 stemmed plants of each species should be planted as a group. The different groups of plants should be distinct from one another in terms of leaf shape and colour. The delicate green, feathered leaves of *Cabomba caroliniana* are shown off to good effect next to the reddish brown leaves of *Rotala macranda* and, similarly, the long, narrow, green leaves of *Hygrophila stricta* go well with the red milfoil *Myriophyllum* "matogrossense". These groups could be dotted around up to the middle of the aquarium, depthwise. The sides can be planted with tall-stemmed specimens which can then be allowed to grow up to the water surface. Any vacant areas on the backdrop can be dotted with the fernlike *Microsorium pteropus*. These are best attached to the backdrop with glass pins. For the centre of the bed it is better to go for bushy plants with a squat growth habit.

Nor should you leave out the water lily, *Nymphaea lotus*, from your planting scheme. This initially grows into a round, large-leaved bush and later forms floating leaves under the surface of the water and these are much favoured as hideaways by labyrinth fish. You should also try to ensure that any plants you choose are fast growers so that they will quickly use up all the available nutrients, eliminating the chance of an excessive algal build up. Only after a few weeks, once the aquarium is fully "run in" and the plants are starting to luxuriate, should you attempt to introduce difficult or slow growing subjects. The precise planting scheme is best left to the individual.

Once the botanical aspect of the decoration is taken care of, the water level can be carefully increased to full depth. After this, a filter must be installed and for an aquarium 130 cm long this should have a capacity of 600 liters per hour. The filter under the pump only needs to be filled with a mechanical filtering medium. It is important that the outlet point for the water should give a horizontal discharge about 2 to 3 cm *beneath* the surface. The resultant water current induces a vigorous movement of the surface water but at the same time avoids an undesirable spray or fountain effect. The stream of water itself should be directed away from the back wall and one third to half way towards the front pane which will produce a relatively good water circulation. Furthermore, practical experience has shown that it is advantageous if the water intake sucks in the water from the same corner where it discharges. The happy side effect of this water movement is that all the decaying organic matter that cannot escape down through the fine gravel is drawn into the filter pot by the water current. A further advantage of the water movement is the continuous supply of nutrients to the plants and the turbulence at the surface means that the water is constantly being enriched with added oxygen. The outmoded method of aeration with an airstone has little to recommend it in such a modern aquarium set up. This is only required now in breeding tanks. The filter pot of the circulating pump can be skilfully concealed behind plants and does not have to offend the eye of the beholder. Motorised filters standing outside the tank and conveying water to and from it through an arrangement of pipes are not best suited for producing a beneficial water movement.

A thermostat then needs to be fitted to regulate the temperature of the aquarium. These are often inserted into the tank but a better solution is to use modern technology and bring the heat regulation equipment out of the tank. This will free the aquarium of dangerous, current carrying apparatus, provided, of course, that you have decided on the TetraPlan heating mat which sits outside the aquarium itself. For heat regulation you should use the TetraStat 1000 electronic thermostat which is very simple to operate and accomplishes its duties from outside the tank. A small, water-tight, low-voltage sensor connected to the TetraStat 1000 will ensure that the water is maintained at precisely the temperature you desire.

This almost "state of the art" aquarium now needs only the right, plant-growth-promoting lighting system. Two possibilities have already been mentioned at the start of our discussion of equipment. When lighting with fluorescent tubes, the rule of thumb is 0.5 Watts per liter of aquarium water. A new fluorescent lighting technique, namely the indium amalgan lamps made by Osram means that the above guidelines are now rather excessively high. These LUMILUX fluorescent tubes mean that there is a light gain of 70 over the Osram de Lux lights. The recommended light level for our purposes here is the LUMILUX 21 and in combination with several fluorescent tubes, LUMILUX 21 and 31. However, this light gain is only achieved in full at an operating temperature of between 30 and 40 °C which says a lot in favour of "open top" operation for the future since far higher temperatures tend to occur in covered aquarium systems when the lighting is in operation — despite ventilating equipment. In spite of the advent of these new, more powerful lights, one should still consider changing used tubes after about six months. After about this period of operation the lighting power of a normal fluorescent tube is reduced by about one third. Added to the change in the lighting capacity, the detrimental effect on plant growth can be considerable. This means that you should establish a regime for regular replacement of the tubes, though where there are severeal of these involved they should not all be changed at the same time but staggered at different intervals.

In the tropical homelands of these labyrinth fish day and night are of almost equal duration, that is to say both day and night last for about 12 hours. This is the diurnal rhythm that you should try to adhere to when lighting your aquarium, so that your lighting is switched on for a twelve hour stretch — without any exception, whether it be a working day or weekend, high day or holiday. In order to ensure that night will fall at more or less the same time, a time switch is highly recommended. The time at which the period of illumination starts is of secondary importance; what does matter is that it should be of twelve hours' duration and start at the same time each day.

Now we come to the final element that could be called of a "technical" nature, namely the plant food carbon which is available in abundance under natural conditions. In the aquarium though it has to be added to the water and thus supplied to plants through certain technical aids. The addition of carbon — which can only be absorbed by plants in a gaseous state as CO_2 and thus make a useful contribution to healthy plant growth — is not, as many people are inclined to think, a recent phenomenon and should not be dismissed as a "new-fangled gimmick". The claim that the aquarists of old knew nothing about such things and still got plants to grow well, is quite erroneous. The old hands of years gone by were a whole lot closer to recognising the importance of carbon dioxide as a growth stimulant for the aquarium than we may realise. As an example of this one might quote the results of research undertaken by K. HEINRICH of the "Seerose" Club in Berlin-Lichtenberg, published in their weekly magazine in 1938. In this article the author states that after the addition of carbon dioxide the fish took on a much better colouring and had a much improved appetite which was probably brought about by the slight acidification of the water due to the carbon dioxide. What is more important is his observation that there was an enormous change in the plants' appearance once the water was enriched with carbon dioxide. The stem diameter of *Ambulia* increased from 0.8 to 1.9 mm; the leaf size of *Aponogeton ulvaceus* rose from 23 × 128 to 45 × 200 mm and that of *Cryptocoryne griffithii* went up from 35 × 65 to 65 × 128 mm. Specimens of *Ceratopteris thalictroides* that started as young plants of 20 mm grew to 270 mm tall in just eight weeks.

The above report shows that the importance of added CO_2 as a nutrient for aquatic plants had been recognised quite early on. It can be done in a variety of ways. Experiments with the so-called "baker's yeast bottle" were soon discontinued because it was not the cleanest of techniques and led indirectly to contamination of the water. Direct additions of carbon dioxide through a nozzle type set-up are very dangerous and can rapidly lead to poisoning of the fish if the dosage is wrong. As aquarium water absorbs varying amounts of carbon dioxide, depending on its lime content, the addition of CO_2 via a diffusor is the simplest and safest method. The simplest solution is to use Tetra CO_2 diffusion tubes that can be fixed with suckers to the lower parts of the side panes, allowing carbon dioxide to be released into the water in the desired amounts. All you need do is work out the appropriate number of tubes to use for the amount of water and carbonate hardness involved. The tubes are filled with CO_2 via the manual control valve and these then supply the plants with vital CO_2 by releasing it into the water.

At this stage the "large aquarium for labyrinth fish" could be deemed to be fully furnished. However, one should still wait another fortnight before putting in the fish because the aquarium has yet to settle down. Constant thermometer checks should be carried out to ensure that the desired temperature is being maintained and all other items of equipment should be given a thorough functional test over this period. At the end of the two weeks the plants will have settled in and in some cases will be growing away.

Here I have tried to describe ways of establishing an aquarium taking account of recent, up to date developments. But for many aquarists these things are already "old hat" and you will have been working along these lines for quite some time already.

If I may just summarize the most important features:

O The stand must be stable and level and should offer an easy, comfortable view of the aquarium.

O The bearing surface must be flat and is covered with a 5 to 10 mm thick polystyrene sheet.

O On this is placed the heating mat whose uniform heat generation produces a slight water movement at tank bed level, thus causing oxygen-rich water to circulate in the bed as well. This does not amount to a suffusion of the bed though, as this would be unacceptable.

O If one decides to have an aquarium backdrop, this should be cut to give a snug fit in the tank.

O The bed consists of an initial layer of fine, dark unwashed gravel; then a layer of gravel mixed with TetraInitial D to promote plant growth; finally a topping of fine, dark, washed gravel.

O After this the pieces of decorative material such as bogwood and lime-free stones are put in and bedded well into the gravel.

O The water is then let in until the tank is half full.

O The larger plants are set out in groups just in front of the back wall and at the sides. Bushy plants and those with a low growth habit occupy the middle sections and the foreground.

O A dense planting scheme with around 200 to 250 plants is about right for an area of 130×40 cm because a wealth of healthy, luxuriant plants is an important factor in water care and healthy water means healthy fish.

O The tank is then filled carefully up to the top.

O A motor pump ensures proper water circulation, oxygen enrichment, the supply of nutrients to the plants and removal of decaying flotsam and debris in the tank. For a container 130 cm long you should install a unit with a minimum capacity of 600 liters per hour.

The type of lighting system you opt for is of secondary importance. What is decisive is the amount of light. As a rule of thumb you can say you need 0.5 Watts per liter of water. The need for a time clock must be stressed once again.

O The light must remain switched on for 12 hours a day following the same daily pattern.

O To stimulate strong, healthy plant growth CO_2 should be added.

O A thermometer is obviously required to check on the temperature.

O The fish should only be put in a fortnight later as the newly established aquarium needs time to stabilize.

O If there appears to be a danger of algae forming at this stage, a number of algae-eating fish can be introduced earlier.

O The first water change should take place two to three weeks after the full stock of fish have been put in. About a third or a quarter of the tank content should be changed and this procedure is then repeated at fortnightly intervals.

An aquarium equipped and decorated along these lines will give a lot of pleasure and be a delightful focus of attention in any living room. On the subject of the "small aquarium for labyrinth fish", all that needs to be said is that it does not differ much from the larger version in general terms. However, you should not allow the length to go below 70 cm. The ideal lighting arrangement for this size of tank is 20 Watt fluorescent tubes which have an overall length of about 66 cm with holders.

In all other technical aspects you can proceed in the same way as for the "large aquarium". The motor pump can be of a lower capacity, say around 200 liters throughput per hour and you could opt for those makes that work under water. But you must at all costs avoid any bubbling, producing the same effect as aeration because this would thwart your strategy for putting carbon dioxide into the water and rob the plants of the CO_2 they need in order to thrive.

Both types of aquarium need regular water changes at two weekly intervals with additions of plant nutrients in the form of complex fertilizers such as Crypto fertilizers, now ideally available in the new EDTA slow release form.

THE ASIATIC LABYRINTH FISH

◆ *Anabas testudineus*
(BLOCH, 1795)

This fish grows up to 25 cm long and is not normally suitable for keeping with small species.

As it occurs in a very wide range of geographical regions, its appearance can vary quite markedly, making comments on its colouring almost superfluous.

Differentiation of the sexes is difficult, though the males are generally darker and have a pointed anal fin.

The

natural habitat
extends over vast areas of South East Asia. As this species has long since been farmed commercially, it is scarcely possible to speculate on its original natural habitat. Nowadays *Anabas testudineus* can be found in Sri Lanka, Thailand, Malaysia, Indonesia, Cambodia and throughout Vietnam into Southern China. They live in a variety of ponds and pools where they lurk amongst the bank vegetation or on the muddy bottom, relying on their excellent camouflage to help them catch their prey. The water quality here is very variable which means that is of secondary importance in captivity. The temperatures fluctuate between 20 and 25 °C, depending on the specific locality and season. As so-called climbing fish they are capable of abandoning a particular site if the prevailing conditions deteriorate and migrating overland to a new, more acceptable stretch of water. In doing so they make use of their pectoral fins, gill covers and the caudal peduncle as means of locomotion. These

Anabas testudineus.

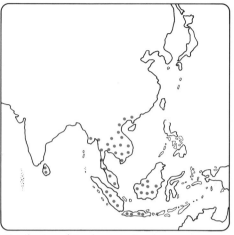

Distribution of *Anabas testudineus*.

trips, often covering many yards to the next water hole, are usually undertaken at night or in the early morning when the ground is still wet.

There are tales of these fish "clambering" their way over distances up to 100 metres hereby their uncanny sense of direction for locating the next pool is quite remarkable. As they are a much prized food in their homelands, their nocturnal peregrinations — which are usually conducted in groups — are regarded as a real bonanza by the local population.

For the

General care

of this species you should provide an aquarium at least 70 cm long, 40 cm wide and

Anabas testudineus migrating overland.

40 cm deep. The bed should be of gravel with a grain size between 1 and 3 mm.

A well planted aquarium is recommended, containing "hardy" aquatic plants like *Vallisneria gigantea,* the giant eel grass, *Anubias lanceolata* and *Anubias nana,* together with large-leaved plants like *Echinodorus cordifolius* and ferns such as *Bolbitis heudelotii.* This is necessary because various forms of this fish, depending on their country of origin, can be avid consumers of tender plants. Bits of bogwood and plenty of cavities should be provided. *Microsorium pteropus* would also be a welcome addition to the planting scheme.

Floating plants like *Ceratopteris pteridoides* or *Pistia stratiotes* provide shade and will give these shy fish a better sense of security.

An aquarium like this can have normal lighting. A good internal filter, like the very efficient Brilliant Filter is highly recommended. The water temperature should lie between 20 and 25 °C reflecting that of its natural conditions.

Water quality is of secondary importance though a water change (one-third of the aquarium content) should be carried out every two weeks as a matter of course. The tank should be well covered because *Anabas testudineus* are not just "wanderers" but good jumpers too. For a community tank you should only choose big and equally robust companion fish, such as medium sized cichlids or gouramis of the genus *Trichogaster* and climbing perches like *Ctenopoma kingsleyae* and *Ctenopoma multispinis.*

As these are predatory fish they should be given a high protein diet. They take TetraMin quite readily as a dietary supplement and they should be fed TetraPhyll as a purely vegetable additive. TetraTips FD also represents a very good, high grade food since it contains beef liver, Tubifex, mosquito larvae and shrimps. If their owner shows proper care and patience these fish become quite tame and can eventually be hand fed.

At the moment little is known about their
breeding.
Anyone who wants to breed this species

should acquire large aquaria at least 160 cm long and around 50 cm wide. The water should be around 20 cm deep and plenty of floating plants are recommended. The fish spawn in open water following a typical writhing courtship. They do not build nests. The eggs rise to the water surface where

Anabas testudineus is a common predator in the paddy fields and associated ditches of South East Asia.

they then develop. Once spawning ist completed, the pair should be seperated and removed from the breeding tank.

Current thinking is that there is a second species that has hitherto been treated as synonymous with *Anabas testudineus* but which in fact represents a completely separate species.

This is

▶ *Anabas oligolepis*
(BLEEKER, 1855)

This second species is thought to differ from *Anabas testudineus* through its higher body shape, fewer scales in the lateral line, a lower number of hard rays and a higher number of soft rays in the dorsal fin. The species also bears shorter pectoral fins and has a longer snout. However, its most conspicuous feature is said to be the absence of the dark spot on the caudal peduncle. This has proved to be a somewhat inconclusive distinguishing mark though, because some specimens do indeed carry this spot. The size is also supposed to be similar to that of *Anabas testudineus* but my field observations in Bangladesh lead me to believe that it is somewhat smaller, reaching an adult length of only 15 to 18 cm. These fish have a very beautiful, dark green colouring enhanced by a delicate coppery sheen of varying extent and intensity. Unfortunately, this colouring has not yet been shown to full effect in the aquarium.

Both species of Anabas live in Bangladesh and inhabit the same kind of biotope in the west of that country. They are very popular as a table fish and are found in great quantities on markets throughout the land.

Their
natural habitat
cannot really be tied down to a particular biotope because they are likely to occur in almost any stretch of water. But they seem to prefer shallow, overgrown, weed-ridden, standing waters with a good cover of water hyacinths. They also live in slow flowing watercourses and some of the larger rivers of the country. The water here is generally soft to medium hard with a neutral to slightly alkaline reaction.

A specimen of *Anabas oligolepis* caught in Bangladesh.

The second species in this genus is

▶ *Belontia hasselti*
(CUVIER, 1831)

This grows to about 20 cm long, with the females being slightly smaller. It is only possible to distinguish the sexes when they are fully grown, at which point the males will display larger dorsal, caudal and anal fins. This species is generally rather shy and not aggressive towards its fellows in the tank. One often gets the impression that they are not in good condition because they will lie resting on the bottom or lean with their sides propped against plants or stones. However, this is part of the normal pattern of behaviour for this species. They must be given a large tank and the aforementioned "large aquarium" must be regarded as an absolute minimum size.

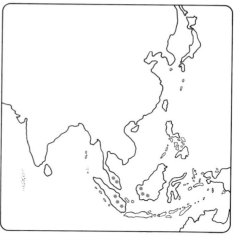

Distribution of *Belontia hasselti*.

The
natural habitat
is Malaysia, Borneo and the island of Sumatra.

Belontia hasselti.

A species that is endemic to Sri Lanka is

▶ *Belontia signata*
(GÜNTHER, 1861)

the comb-tail paradise fish, which grows to 12 cm long and has a reputation for being rather aggressive. In fact these fish are rather shy and show their "true colours" in both the literal and behavioural sense only when kept in conditions that really suit them. Sexual differentiation is difficult and the only way of recognizing a female is by the swollen belly when spawning time approaches.

The
natural habitat
comprises narrow, slow-flowing streams but also some of the bigger watercourses in the lowlands of the island. This species has also been found in the area of the Kottowa

Belontia signata.

Forest *(see also Malpulutta kretseri)*. It leads a very retiring, concealed existence near the river's edge, at the foot of steep banks, tucked away amongst plants.

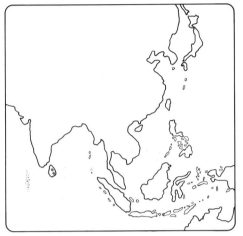

Asiatic distribution of *Belontia signata*.

The water quality they need is shown in Table 4 (Page 96) but for

breeding

these conditions do not necessarily apply. If one wants to breed *Belontia signata* they should be given a largish aquarium at least 100 × 50 × 40 cm in size. There should be plenty of plants available and the water temperature can lie between 27 and 30 °C. If a pair of comb-tailed paradise fish over 9 cm long are put into a breeding tank of this sort they will breed quite readily once they get to know each other.

This species builds a bubble nest as the eggs are released, although in some very rare cases they may build a bubble nest before spawning. The eggs are laid after the typical entangled courtship rites. They are then gathered under the surface and surrounded with air bubbles and secretions from the mouth. Both parents participate in caring for the brood and this protective behaviour may continue until the fry are six weeks old — a phenomenon that is quite rare amongst labyrinth fish.

For the

general care

of *Belontia signata* a largish aquarium, 130 cm or over, is needed and the recommendations for the "larger aquarium for labyrinth fish" apply. Lots of plants, bogwood and rock structures with caves will make up an ideal environment, complemented by a few floating plants to provide surface cover. Gravel with a grain diameter of up to 3 mm should cover the bottom. With a dark backdrop these combtail paradise fish will feel at home in the company of other larger species of fish. But be warned about the dangers for smaller, more delicate species — neon tetras for example, would be hard pressed to survive in such company.

The normal water temperature can be around 25 °C and the water should not be too hard or have too high a mineral content. This can be checked quickly and easily with the TetraTest GH and TetraTest KH indicators. Figures of around 15 °d general hardness and 12 °d carbonate hardness with a pH of up to 7 should be the upper limit.

A *Belontia signata* habitat in the south of the island of Sri Lanka.

One of the species of fighting fish less commonly kept is

▶ *Betta anabatoides*
(BLEEKER, 1850)

which grows to an overall length of 10 cm. Unfortunately, few people have had the opportunity of studying this fish until recently. Luckily, a recent catching expedition succeeded in bringing back a few specimens to Germany for observation. Sexual differentiation is difficult, though the males are rather more intensely coloured and have somewhat longer fins.

Their
natural habitat
is probably restricted to southern Borneo, more correctly known as Kalimantan, the

Indonesian part of the island of Borneo. Whether or not it occurs on the neighbour-

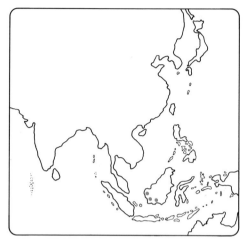

Asiatic distribution of *Betta anabatoides*.

Betta anabatoides.

26

ing islands of Sumatra and Singapore is questionable. However, its distribution range in southern Borneo is wide and it can be caught in large numbers alongside *Betta edithae*.

The watercourses here are very clear and have a light brownish tinge. The water is very soft and low in minerals with a conductivity measured at between 5 and 30 micro-siemens at water temperatures of 27 to 30 °C. Measurements of the pH gave results in the very acidic range with values around 4.8 and lower. The species likes to stay near to the banks in areas thick with vegetation.

The following conclusions were drawn in respect of the

general care

of this species: the tanks should not be too small, a length of at least 100 cm being advisable. As it is very tolerant by nature, several specimens can be kept together. Areas of the aquarium should be densely planted as it tends to be a timid sort.

As far as

breeding

is concerned, no one has had any success as yet. *Betta anabatoides* is one of the mouth-brooding species of fighting fish.

Flooded ditches at the end of a jungle river in South Borneo. This is the habitat of various species of *Betta*.

One of the largest, bubble nest spawning fighting fish, imported for the first time in 1913, is

◗ *Betta bellica*
(SAUVAGE, 1884)

The Latin derivation of its name "bellica" — "warlike", "belligerent", "aggressive", is only remotely applicable to this species and would probably be more appropriately ascribed to *Betta splendens*. *Betta bellica* attains an overall length of 11 cm. It is possible to differentiate the sexes when they are only half grown. The male fish are more deeply coloured and have somewhat longer fins. A particularly noticeable feature is the slight "fraying" of the caudal and anal fins. Whereas the females retain a rounded shape to their caudal fin, the middle section of the males' caudal fin lengthens and becomes lanceolate. The species under discussion here comes from the Perak region of Malaysia, part of the Malaysian peninsula. VIERKE found them living in a roadside ditch in Ayer Hitam. The water there was very soft and highly acidic. The pH value was 4.6 and the electrical conductivity was measured at 33 microsiemens at a water temperature of 28 °C. If this fish is to be

Asiatic distribution of *Betta bellica*.

kept successfully and especially if you intend to try breeding it, your water quality should be something approaching the above. The aquaria should be densely planted with particular attention being paid to those that reach up to the surface and to floating plants. The provision of pieces of bogwood and hideaways would also prove beneficial. Breeding is still rather problematical. Breeding pairs are best kept away from other fish.

Betta Bellica.

It has only been a couple of years since Dr. Jörg VIERKE first described the species

▶ *Betta climacura*
(VIERKE, 1988)

This is a mouth-brooding fighting fish that attains a total length of about 12 cm. In his description of this species VIERKE noted: "The live colouring of this species is very variable. Only the males have the laddering in the caudal fin. In reflected light the scales may shine greenish or bluish or even golden, depending on how the light catches them. There are none of the typical scales in the gill cover region, so characteristic of *Betta pugnax*. When in spawning condition, the females display the black pattern so typical of the species, namely three stripes on the body, the middle one beginning just behind the eye and running directly above the base of the pectoral fin before joining up with the lower stripe. This begins only at about the level of the fifth body scale. The united middle and lower stripes end in the caudal peduncle in a conglomerate spot that may be more or less noticeable. The upper stripe is

Asiatic distribution of *Betta climacura*.

often less clearly defined". The species comes from Borneo and is found in many regions of Sarawak. I identified this fish in the Sungei Sekerang (Skrang River) in the area around Bandar Sri Aman in Sarawak in 1980.

Betta climacura.

Another species that has only been known for a short time is

◗ *Betta coccina*
(VIERKE, 1979),

which is a peaceable, bubble nest building fighting fish that grows to a total length of 6 cm. It ranks amongst the most magnificently coloured of the genus *Betta*.

The first specimens were imported via the firm Vivaria Indonesia of Jakarta which had caught this species near to Jambi in central Sumatra. Unfortunately no details of the ecological background here are known. In 1986 NAGY also reported finding them in localities in the south of the Malayan peninsula.

We found *Betta coccina* in blackwater as well as clear water. The water values in the source region showed a pH of between 4.1 and 4.6 with a conductivity between 27 and 35 microsiemens both in the rainy season and during periods of drought when only the main streams were carrying any water. A few hundred metres downstream the pH value had already dropped to 3.8 but in contrast the conductivity had risen to 50 to 75 microsiemens. If you shook out the free

Asiatic distribution of *Betta coccina*.

carbon dioxide, the pH value rose to between 5.5 and 5.8. The temperature was between 25 and 27 °C.

For their general care in the aquarium this gives some interesting consequences. The water quality needs to be good, soft and acidic. In my experience a pH of 4.5 seems best.

Betta coccina.

As recently as 1979 a further, newly discovered mouth brooding fighting fish has come to light through the efforts of Ms E. KORTHAUS and Dr. W. FOERSCH, namely:

▶ *Betta edithae*
(VIERKE, 1984)

A number of specimens were discovered by them in the jungle swamps of Kalimantan (South Borneo) near the banks of a water ditch. The biggest specimen caught to date was 65 mm long. It is most decidedly one of the mouth brooders. Breeding experiments conducted by FOERSCH have shown that this fish spawns like the other mouth brooding *Betta* species encountered hitherto and that the male then gathers the fry in his mouth and releases them only after about 12 days of paternal care. FOERSCH discovered that there may be in excess of 125 of these youngsters.

Asiatic distribution of *Betta edithae*.

The species is widespread in Kalimantan and comparatively easy to breed, being a very productive sort.

Betta edithae.

31

A small species discovered in 1978 and also belonging to the "foerschi-strohi group" is

Betta foerschi
(VIERKE, 1909)

named after Dr. Walter FOERSCH who has done stalwart service over the last few years with his own expeditions and intensive studies in the labyrinth fish field. This species of fish grows to about 65 mm in length. They are very slim creatures and very aggressive towards one another. Generally though, they have shown themselves to be very timid. The sexes are relatively easy to tell apart. The vertical stripes on the gill covers turn a brilliant shade of gold when the males become agitated whereas those of the female become blood red.

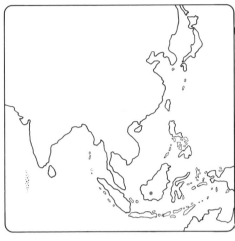

Asiatic distribution of *Betta foerschi*.

The

natural habitat
of these fish lies around 75 km north west of Sampit in the area around Palangan. The waters here are very soft and acidic (pH 5.2) with temperatures around 25 °C. Nothing is yet known about their reproductive biology.

Betta foerschi.

The fighting fish

▶ *Betta fusca*
(REGAN, 1909)

Asiatic distribution of *Betta fusca*.

has seldom been seen in aquaria until now. These rarely imported fish belong to the so-called circle of "pugnax forms" and undoubtedly fall into the category of mouth brooding fighting fish, although nobody has yet substantiated this with information on successful breeding. The photograph here shows a specimen I gratefully received from Drs. YUWONO of Vivaria-Indonesia. J. SCHMIDT identified it as *betta fusca* after some intensive research. These fish originate from the area around Pakanbaru in the Rian district of central Sumatra. *Betta fusca* shows many parallels to *Betta pugnax*. Like *Betta pugnax*, the males display deep green coloured scales on the gill covers. As a further distinguishing feature, J. SCHMIDT writes: "The body shape of *Betta fusca* remains slimmer than in other large, pointed-finned, mouth brooding fighting fish. The body of *Betta fusca* is reddish brown and the dots on the scales of the male form a linear pattern that is typical of the species. The fins are long, extended affairs but not quite as extreme as in other species and in some forms of *Betta pugnax*. The mouth is apical, slightly downward pointing, as in *Betta pugnax*."

Betta fusca.

33

One of the smaller, very colourful, bubble nesting fighting fish is

▶ *Betta imbellis*
(LADIGES, 1975)

This species is renowned for its peaceable nature and only grows to 5 cm in length. The males develop quite long fins and are a dark blue to black colour on their body. The gill covers, the edges of the body scales and the fins are zoned with areas of a verdigris-like sheen, with the caudal fin having a black-edged band to it. In contrast, the females have short red and blue fins and a brown body. When displaying, they acquire a yellow and brown patterning on the body.

The
natural habitat
indicated in the first description of these fish was stated to be the area around Kuala Lumpur, the capital of Malaysia. Since then it has been found in other localities too. I have caught specimens on the island of Phuket, 500 kilometers to the north, off the coast of southern Thailand. They were living in parts of the paddy fields that still had water in them, in full ditches and in pond-like stretches of water.

Betta imbellis lives predominantly in stands of vegetation or in overgrown bank zones. I have caught these fish on the island of Penang where they could likewise be found in little culverts near the rice fields but also in little water filled hollows in the ground no bigger than your hand and in marshy or flooded areas. I also found *Betta imbellis* on the east coast of the main Malaysian peninsula in a natural stream near the South China Sea at Kuantan. I have also come across this species on Sumatra, around 30 km south west of Medan.

Betta imbellis.

The

general care

of this species is not problematical. Aquaria 70 cm long by 40 cm wide and 30 cm deep are suitable. This species should only be kept with other small, placid natured types. Several pairs can be kept together as they are not aggressive towards one another. The males only become intolerant when they are staking out the area under their bubble nest and little disputes may arise. If a group of *Betta imbellis* has grown up together they will continue to live harmoniously as adults. It is only if strange adult specimens are introduced that problems arise. The aquarium should be well planted with plenty of bogwood roots and hideaways included in the decoration.

The water temperature can be around the 25 °C mark but if you want to admire their colours in their full splendour the temperature should be raised slightly to 28 °C. Floating plants like *Ceratopteris pteridoides*, *Riccia flutans* or *Pistia stratiotes* also belong in the scheme of things. The water should be filtered through an internal Brillant Filter. The aquarium should be adequately lighted at a rate of 0.5 Watts per liter of water.

Breeding

this species is not difficult. The males build their bubble nests under the leaves of floating plants and frequently under pieces of bogwood and overhanging rocks close to the surface. The nest has a diameter of about 5 cm. A female that is ready to spawn — recognisable by the yellow and brown ringed pattern on her body — follows the male to a place just below the bubble nest after a brief courtship and it is here that spawning takes place. The entire act of spawning takes two hours and is a very harmonious affair. The female is not a victim of the "battered wife" syndrome as is often the case with the Siamese fighting fish, *Betta splendens*. The male does, however, entwine his body around that of his mate in exactly the same way.

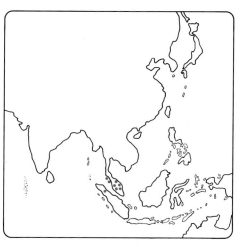

Asiatic distribution of *Betta imbellis*.

Table No. 1

Locality:	Phuket Island South Thailand
Clarity:	slightly turbid to clear
Colour:	milky to colourless
pH value:	7.0
D general hardness	8 — 10 (average)
D carbonate hardness	not measured
Conductivity:	270 — 540 micro-siemens at 34 °C
Nitrite:	0.05 mg/l
Water depth:	up to 50 cm
Water movement:	none
Water temperature:	34 °C
Date of tests:	6. 3. 1976 Time: 11.00

As the eggs emerge, they only slip a few millimetres out of the ovipositor to a spot just below the pectoral fin from whence they are only released when the male loosens his grip of the female, turning her on to her side. As they fall out, the male then gathers them in his mouth. Before the female awakens from the immobility that grips her during the act of spawning — a sort of "rigor" of birth — all the eggs of a spawning phase, about 5–15 in all — are carried to the nest by the male. Over the next few days the size of the bubble nest may grow to 10 cm. The male takes diligent care of the clutch until it hatches after about 75 hours and the young fry swim free. At this point it is preferable if the parents are removed although they do not molest the fry generally. TetraMikroMin should be given as the first food as this is particularly well suited for raising youngsters, being very fine-particled. It also fulfills their nutritional requirements to the fullest degree. Give small amounts several times a day. As the task of raising them to maturity does not present any difficulties, this relatively new species will no doubt soon become a standard feature in the aquaria of fans of labyrinth fish.

Densely overgrown bank zones like this one here, near Kuantan in West Malaysia, are the natural habitat of *Betta imbellis*.

It was as late as 1986 before it was possible to import from the eastern part of West Malaysia a very large growing, mouth brooding species of fighting fish that is known as

▶ *Betta macrophthalma*
(REGAN, 1909)

The basis for these further observations was a single specimen that was caught by Walter SCHAR in August 1985 in a small roadside stream next to the Kuantan to Kuala Lumpur highroad, 232 kilometres out of KL or 22 km from Kuantan.

This fish is without doubt one of the biggest in the genus, having already attained a total length of 13.5 cm at the time it was caught. In the aquarium it continued to grow to 14.5 cm and as such represents the biggest type of fighting fish hitherto known. A notable feature is the colouring, as described by KRUMMENACHER. According to him, the species has a "magnificent colouring" of brownish red that lightens towards the belly. The fins likewise are brownish red. But the most conspicuous feature of all are the deep black lips and the lower snout which is also a deep black.

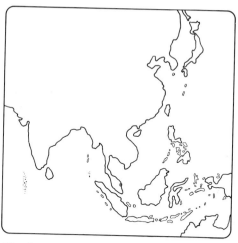

Distribution of *Betta waseri*.

When frightened, *Betta macrophthalma* displays a dark, broad longitudinal stripe as its main marking. For a long time the species was known as *Betta waseri*. In their natural biotope the fish live in clear, flowing, very soft and very acidic waters partly overgrown with weeds. They live together with *Parospromenus nagyi*, *Betta pugnax (?)* and *Betta tussyae*.

A young specimen of *Betta macrophthalma* (also known as *Betta waseri*).

One of the most colourful of the mouth brooding fighting fish must be

▶ *Betta macrostoma*
(REGAN, 1909)

Its striking body colour distinguishes it from all other mouth brooding fighting fish known to date. T. SCHULZ was the first person to import it to Europe and carry out detailed observations in 1984. *Betta macrostoma* grows to a length of about 10 cm. It is the very large mouth that impressed the original describer, REGAN, to the extent that he included the feature in its name, "macrostoma" = "large mouthed". At the time he was working only from preserved specimens. Now we are able to appreciate the true colours of this magnificent fish. Its blue mouth and the yellow gill covers set against the orange and brown body are its most noteworthy features. However, what is claimed to be the characteristic feature of the males, namely the dark, light-edged spot on the lower rear end of the dorsal fin is not present in all specimens. Sexual differentia-

Asiatic distribution of *Betta macrostoma*.

tion is only possible in larger, more mature individuals. Whilst the females are likely to still keep the dual longitudinal marking of the youngsters, the males are more vividly coloured, without any longitudinal stripes and with fins that show a coloured pattern

Betta macrostoma, ♀

to some extent. They behave quite peacefully towards other species of their own size but tussles tend to occur.

The
natural habitat
is found in Sarawak on the island of Borneo. Thomas SCHULZ caught this species in the upper reaches of the Mendaram River (Sungai Mendaram) near Rampayoh in the Sultanate of Brunei in north Borneo. His records indicate that the water there was very soft and acidic. The pH value was 4.3.

For their
general care
you should provide an adequately sized aquarium, densely planted in parts with good quality, acidic water that is low in minerals. Extremely clean water with a low bacterial count is absolutely essential if they are to be kept with any degree of success because this species is very susceptible to infections. A varied diet is likewise very important, above all containing plenty of live insects and their larvae. Unfortunately, the care of this species is still not without its problems.

Its
breeding
behaviour could be compared with that of *Betta unimaculata* (SCHULZ, 1985). However, in *Betta macrostoma*, as in the other well known, mouth brooding *Betta species*, the female picks up the eggs in her mouth from the anal fin of the male once they have been fertilized. Unlike the other species, she does not "spit" them in front of the male's mouth but rather passes them over in little batches from mouth to mouth. Their offspring take about twenty days to hatch and when they are ready to leave the close attentions of their father's mouth, the youngsters are between seven and nine millimeters long and capable of handling freshly hatched nauplia of *Artemia salina*. If fed on a varied diet and with regular water changes, they will reach sexual maturity themselves after about 6 months.

Betta macrostoma, ♂

39

The smallest bubble nesting fighting fish known to date is

▶ Betta persephone
(SCHALLER, 1986)

This dwarflike creature only reaches a total length of 3 cm when fully grown. This unmarked, dark greyish green to black coloured species often has deep dark green dorsal, caudal and anal fins. Males carry a light, conspicuous edging to the front upper art of the dorsal fin and white tips to the ventral fins. Females are somewhat more rounded and their fins are rather shorter. As far as we can tell, these fish are very placid and easy to keep in an aquarium that offers the right accommodation. Their distribution covers parts of the Malaysian peninsula. According to SCHALLER (1986) the locality where the original specimens were found is a stretch of water on "Asian Highway No. 2, about three kilometers north of Ayer Hitam. It is the second outlet (square tubular bridge) on the second hollow as you go northwards".

This *Betta* secies lives in waters that are very soft and in some cases highly acidic, depending on the amounts of rain. A conductivity level of up to 100 microsiemens and a pH of around 5 are suitable for their general care and breeding. *Betta persephone* leads a very retiring, concealed existence in

Asiatic distribution of *Betta persephone*.

the wild and spends much of its life hidden away between roots and foliage.

According to SCHALLER's notes, in those seasons when there are frequent falls of rain, these fish can often be found amongst the mass of roots in the undergrowth of the forest vegetation, above the flooded ground and the layers of leaves. However, as the water level falls, the fish slide under the layers of leaves, looking for any puddles of water they may find there.

Betta persephone.

Belonging amongst the smaller mouth brooding Betta species and only reimported again towards the end of the seventies is

▶ *Betta picta*
(CUVIER and VALENCIENNES, 1846)

which reaches a total length of up to 6 cm and displays a marked degree of sexual dimorphism when adult. Males have a larger, more powerfully built head and are more deeply coloured. To date specimens with a variety of forms of colouring and patterning have been found, no doubt attributable to different natural factors. Two distinct variants are known, referred to at present as the "Sumatra and Java colour types". Whereas the females of the Sumatra type display a pronounced spotted or flecked pattern in the area of the anal fin, these features are absent in specimens from Java. In terms of morphological measuring data both forms are identical (VIERKE, 1983). *Betta rubra* from Sumatra and *Betta trifasciata* from Java are currently regarded as being synonymous with *Betta picta*.

In its

general care

it has proved to be unproblematical. Nor is it demanding in terms of water quality for

breeding

This species will reproduce freely even in smallish aquaria, provided it is offered some well-planted areas with sufficient hideaways. Their spawning behaviour is similar to that described for *Betta pugnax*. On leaving the shelter of the "parental home" the fry will have attained a length of around 6 mm and immediately take newly hatched nauplia of *Artemia salina*.

The area described here as its

natural habitat

is part of its distributing range in Java.

A locality described by REGAN as a site on which *Betta picta (trifasciata)* has been caught is Ambarawa in Central Java. Here are a few notes from my collecting trip made

Betta picta — male at front, female behind.

in January 1986 which took us in a northerly direction out of Yogjakarta in Central Java. The road went up continuously from the plains up into the mountains and then led eastwards past the Borobudur district via the towns of Magelang, Secang and Jambu to Ambarawa. The highest upland areas appeared to lie between Magelang and Ambarawa. The road is in a good state, allowing us to drive along at a good speed. In the town of Ambarawa a small side road branches off to Muncul and, according to the map, then leads to Salatiga in the south east. Countless narrow streams — fast flowing in the rainy season (January) — and small rivers run down to the road. Every usable piece of land is devoted to rice growing. The vegetation here is very dense and luxuriant. Muncul lies close to the lake. It has a stream running through it with a swimming pool on its bank. Our attempts at catching fish in this stream, which was very fast flowing, were unsuccessful. To the right of the swimming pool's car ark there was a concrete-lined water collection tank, measuring 10 × 35 m. The water depth was about 70 cm. A feeder brook and water continuously flowing out of the bed (lava sand) provided a constant exchange of water and throughflow. This gave rise to movement in the water that might perhaps best be described as a gentle current. In this concrete tank the water was very clean and clear without any discernible colour. Where there was a dense covering of floating plants the temperature was 23.9; at a depth of 10 cm it was 22.8 and at 50 cm 22.3 °C. In amongst this blanket of floating plants and in the zones that were overgrown with floating leaves, including banana leaves, numerous *Betta picta (trifasciata)* were to be found together with countless guppies. In some cases they were adult males with a brood in their mouth i. e. some had eggs and others almost fully formed youngsters. Seemingly, the fish have found their way into this concrete tank through the link with the stream and live here in absolutely optimum conditions, given that there are no predatory fish present. It is likely that this species of *Betta* is also to be found in the rice fields (the

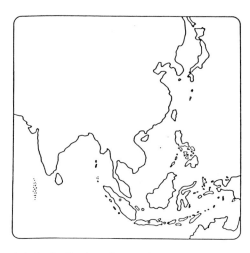

Asiatic distribution of *Betta picta*.

terraced system is used) and their irrigation channels. The local rice farmers said that this was the case but our attempts at catching them there were without success.

A second locality lies around 50 kilometers to the west of here, similarly at an elevation of about 500 meters. Here too we are talking about extensive mountainous regions that are used for rice growing. The spot where the fish were caught lies just a few hundred meters outside of the town of Pikatan. There were two foot wide water ditches on either side of the path and as a result of frequent falls of rain the water on this sloping ground was in constant motion. In places the water was moving over cultivated land too, In the vegetation-free streams and ditches all that could be seen in the way of fish were some fast swimming barbs. We discovered a multitude of *Betta picta (trifasciata)* in the extensive areas of land flooded to a depth of 3 cm and covered with a dense tangle of grass and similar plants. In a short space of time around 15 of this species were caught, including several mouth brooding males.

The species in question was the same as that mentioned above. It is possible that there are colour variants. The individuals caught here had gold coloured gill covers. The water here was also relatively cool at a temperature of 23.2 °C.

One species that is not a bubble nester is

▶ *Betta pugnax*
(CANTOR, 1850)

a mouth brooding species that grows up to 10 cm long. The males are resplendent with their very beautiful, glowing, patina green rows of scales on their dark, grey-brown body. The gill areas are the same colour, as is the extended ventral fin and parts of the edges of the dorsal, caudal and anal fins. The females have somewhat shorter fins and are less vividly coloured.

The
natural habitat
is found in Thailand, West Malaysia and the island of Penang. These fish usually live in fast flowing watercourses amongst thick bank vegetation, often preferring areas where the current is less strong. The localities where this fish is found are predominantly at higher elevations. Mountain streams with very clear, clean and soft water, in parts only 90 cm wide and 50 cm deep, with lots of stones, a fine, sandy bed and largish stands of aquatic plants make up the natural habitat of this species.

In the rainy season the water temperature lies around 22 °C and only rises to 26 °C in the drought period, despite the intensity of the sun's rays.

The
general care
of these fish does not present any problems at all. An aquarium upwards of 70 cm long, 40 cm wide and 30 cm high is recommended. You can use either the "small" aquarium or the "large aquarium for labyrinth fish". Tanks with a copious selection of healthy plants and lots of opportunities to

Betta pugnax.

hide in cavities and amongst pieces of bogwood should be provided for these often very shy and generally rather retiring fish. The water temperature can be between 22 and 25 °C and the water quality should, as far as possible, be in the soft, slightly acidic range. A good filtration system over filter peat and motor-driven is advisable or over activated peat where the water is medium hard to hard. Adequate lighting at a rate of 0.5 Watts per liter should be provided and the aquarium is best sited in a quiet spot.

Give them plenty of high grade food. TetraMin is a favourite snack.

For
breeding
very soft, slightly acidic water and a temperature of 26 to 27 °C are required. The water level should only stand at a depth of 10 to 12 cm and there should be no shortage of floating plants like *Pistia stratiotes* and *Ceratopteris pteridoides*.

Betta pugnax is a mouth brooder and spawns near the tank bottom, dispensing with the bubble nest. The pair entwine their bodies and the eggs emerge to fall on to the slightly arched anal fin of the male from where the female picks them up in her mouth once she has disentangled herself. The spawning phases take place at quite lengthy intervals, almost always at the same place in the aquarium. Between the individual bouts of the courtship the female spits the eggs out in front of her partner's mouth one at a time for him to snap up and retain. On occasions the male may spit the eggs back at the female so that something of a "ball game" seems to develop. On conclusion of the spawning procedure — which can take up to 5 hours — the male will retire to the protection of a densely planted zone. About 10 days later the fully developed youngsters are allowed to leave the shelter of their father's mouth and need to be fed on finely pulverised food like MikroMin. It is advisable to ensure good water quality, including filtration over a heavy duty, easily cleaned Brillant-Filter. The water should be changed regularly (one third of the tank's

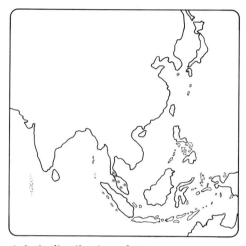

Asiatic distribution of *Betta pugnax*.

Table No. 2

Locality:	Penang Island West Malaysia Road out of Telok Bahang direction of Balik Pula, in the mountains, elevation approx. 300 m above sea level
Clarity:	very clear
Colour:	none
pH value:	6.5
D general hardness	under 1 °dH
D carbonate hardness	under 1 °dH
Conductivity:	25 microsiemens at 26 °C
Nitrite:	0.00 mg/l
Water depth:	up to 50 cm
Water movement:	fast flowing
Water temperature:	26 °C
Date of tests:	27. 11. 1977
Time:	17.00

contents every fortnight), because clean, healthy water promotes the growth of the fry.

Apparently the smallest species of fighting fish yet discovered originates from the Kapuas area and is known as

▶ *Betta rutilans*
WITTE u. KOTTELAT, 1991

These vivid red coloured fish only reach a total length of 3.0 cm when fully grown, as far as we can tell. The fish we caught were some 2 cm long. At this stage the fish were already a bright red colour and displayed their conspicuous, "luminous" green eyes. From its external appearance one would place this species in the "coccina-tussyae group", though it does not have any spots on its flanks. However, there are some astonishing differences in its reproductive biology. Whilst *B. coccina* and *B. tussyae* belong amongst the bubble nest builders, our observations have revealed that this little new species is a mouth brooder. While it is true that we do not have any conclusive study data, many of the procedures and characteristics observed in "phantom" matings point clearly to mouth brooding. Hitherto it has only been possible to differentiate between the sexes during actual mating.

Betta rutilans from Anjungan comes from a region north east of Pontianak, between the towns of Sungei Penjuh and Anjungan.

Asiatic distribution of *Betta rutilans*.

We discovered this species 8 km south west of Anjungan on the road from Pontianak to Mandor in West Kalimantan (Kalimantan Barat). The water in question was a little marshy stream, a more or less typical black-water biotope. The very dark brown coloured, clear water was very soft. Measurements showed an electrical conductivity figure of 39 microsiemens at a water temperature of 27.6 °C. The pH value was 4.5.

Betta spec. rutilans.

45

An extremely beautiful but unfortunately very rare species of fighting fish is one described as recently as 1972 by Dr. Werner LADIGES, namely

▶ *Betta smaragdina*
(LADIGES, 1972)

whereby its total length, as indicated in the first description, is just 6 cm. Dietrich SCHALLER, who caught some of these fish in Thailand and, significantly, brought them back to Germany for observation, reports that this new species can grow to 7 cm long. Compared with the females, the males possess longer fins but both sexes are vividly coloured. In her courtship and spawning attire the female acquires broad, light cross stripes around her body.

The

natural habitat

is the area around the settlement of Nong Khai in north eastern Thailand. Nong Khai lies on the river Mekong on the border with Laos, near the capital Vientiane.

As, for some inexplicable reason, a good deal of wrong information has been passed on about the locations in which this species was found, details of its natural habitat have also been misleading. D. SCHALLER himself recently revised his notes. It is not the region around the town of Nakhon Ratchasima, formerly known as Korat, that represents the range of *Betta smaragdina* but the Korat plateau with the town of Non Khai (Non Chai) which lies 400 kilometers to the

Betta smaragdina.

46

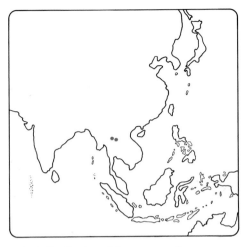

Asiatic distribution of *Betta smaragdina*.

north. The same thing also applies to *Trichopsis schalleri*. I visited this region in the middle of 1979 and caught *Betta smaragdina* there. The first named locality clearly falls within the same catchment areas as *Betta splendens*. The areas around Nong Khai, approximately 50 km across from east to west and down to within some 20 km of the town of Khon Kaen some 160 km to the south, constitute the range in which I have encountered *Betta smaragdina*.

I made another discovery too, namely that this fish is also used as a fighting fish in this area, which would seem to contradict descriptions of the species' nature as "peaceable". According to the organisers of fish fights in Nong Khai, the most aggressive specimens are caught in the district of Udon Thani which lies 53 kilometers to the south. I was able to verify that most of these fish are indistinguishable in terms of fearlessness and aggression from the short-finned species *Betta splendens* which is generally used for such purposes in this part of the world. Moreover, the above discovery also represents a considerable reduction in the range of *Betta splendens*, as this species does not occur in this locality. The extent to which *Betta smaragdina's* range extends northwards over the Mekong or whether this great river constitutes a natural barrier, has not yet been established.

Betta smaragdina lives in stretches of water like paddy fields, in ditches, in small ponds and marshes and often in muddy patches between clumps of plants.

With the onset of the rainy season, when the water level rises or the rice plantations are flooded, these pockets are turned into larger expanses of water and these fish see an end to their isolated existence.

The

general care

of these fish does not present problems. They should be provided with well planted tanks. As they do not tolerate other individuals of the same species, you should only keep one male in an aquarium together with several females. They are suited to both the "small" and the "large aquarium for labyrinth fish".

The water temperature should be around 25 °C and, if possible, the water quality should not be hard or limey. As these fish are rather timid in the presence of other species, they should only be kept with other non-aggressive types. Labyrinth fish like the *Colisa* and *Trichopsis* species are suitable.

For

breeding

these fish require a tank 70 cm long by 40 cm wide and 30 cm deep. One half of the tank is planted with *Hygrophila polysmera*, the Indian water star, or *Hygrophila corymbus*, planted up to the surface, and in the other half two or three stems of *Cabomba caroliniana*, Carolinian fanwort, will suffice. The vacant part of the surface can be partly covered with floating plants of the species *Ceratopteris pteridoides* and *Riccia flutans*, the crystalwort. The water temperature should be raised to 28 °C. As bed material, use gravel with a grain size of 1 to 3 mm. One or two largish stones can be positioned between the clumps of plants as hiding places for the female. A single pair should be used for breeding. *Betta smaragdina* is a bubble nester and positions its nest at the surface. If your breeding attempts are to be successful, soft water is advisable.

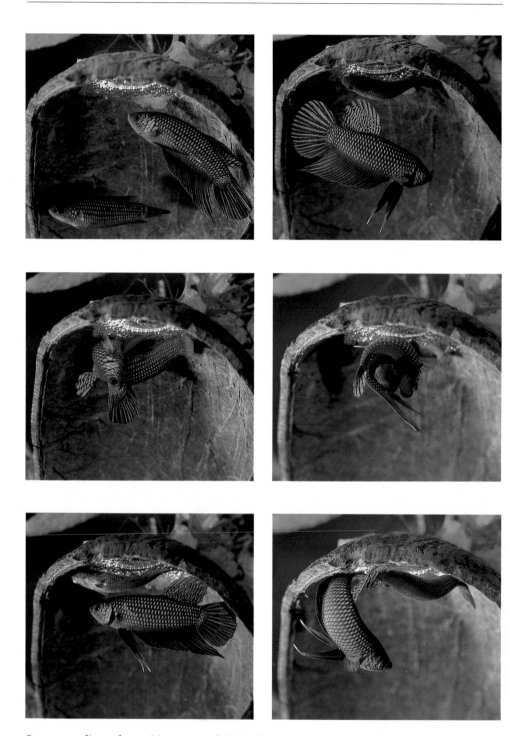

Betta smaragdina prefers cavities or concealed holes for spawning and nest building.

An interesting, largish species of fighting fish that has not yet clearly been classified is

▶ *Betta spec. affin. anabatoides*

from the Kapuas area. In comparison with *Betta anabatoides,* these fish are distinguished by a less powerfully built head with rather different markings. The parts around the gills show a variable amount of green colouring. Another interesting characteristic is the flecking on the membranes of the dorsal and anal fins. It is possible that the fish reach a total length of around 9 cm and are thus somewhat smaller. Presumably, they are also mouth brooders. Norbert NEUGE-BAUER managed to catch some of them on our 1990 expedition between the towns of Sungei Penjuh and Anjungan. The locality in which they were found was a real blackwater biotope with dark brown, clear, gently flowing, very soft and highly acidic water with a pH of between 4.5 and 5.4.

Asiatic distribution of *Betta spec. affin. anabatoides.*

Betta spec. affin. anabatoides.

Another small but very colourful species of fighting fish belonging to the sphere of the "coccina-tussyae" types is

▶ *Betta spec. affin. coccina*

These new fish, very similar to the species *Betta coccina*, were caught on a collecting trip to Sarawak. They attain a total length of about 4.5 cm. Both sexes exhibit an intense dark red body colour. Compared to *B. coccina,* these fish are somewhat smaller and the conspicuous green spot on the side of the body that is typical of the species is larger in the males. Females also have a spot on the side of their body but this remains much smaller. They are bubble nest builders. Soft, acidic water is essential for their general care. All other aspects of water quality are also of prime importance. It appears that the species was imported for the first time by KRUMMENACHER, KETTNER and WITTE.

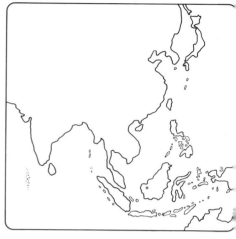

Asiatic distribution of *Betta spec. affin. coccina.*

Betta spec. affin. coccina.

In 1988 we succeeded in importing for the first time another member of the "foerschistrohi" group, the little, mouth brooding, fighting fish species, known for a couple of years as *Betta foerschi* but which, in the light of the latest available information, should best be classified as

▶ *Betta spec. affin. foerschi*
from Tangkiling.

In their bodily shape and colour and in their fin growth these fish differ only slightly from *Betta foerschi* which has only been imported again in 1990. Further observations will be required before it can be established whether these are in fact distinct species. We encountered *Betta spec. affin. foerschi* in 1988 just 35 km north of Palangkaraya on the road to Kasungan. About 3 km beyond the town of Tangkiling as you drive north, there was a small stream that crossed the road. The gently flowing water had a low mineral content and was coloured a deep dark brown. The bank zones and often entire stretches of water were overgrown with masses of plants. *Betta spec. affin. foerschi* was only to be found in very shallow bank zones between plants and dead leaves. With *Betta spec. affin. foerschi* we have been able to import not just the most interesting species of fighting fish from the standpoint of behavioural science but without doubt one of the most beautifully coloured, smaller mouth brooders of this genus.

Breeding
of this species has proved successful on many occasions already and their behaviour at this time is quite remarkable. Without question, they are the most interesting species in terms of breeding behaviour. It is a vivid illustration of the transition between bubble nest builders and mouth brooders. Many aspects and procedures equate closely to those of the bubble nest spawners whereby many parallels can be drawn between these and *Betta splendens*.

On the other hand, there are also typical behavioural characteristics of the mouth brooding Betta species in evidence. The aggression its fellows described above and said to be so typical of the species has not yet been seen by this observer. That these fish are not exactly placid but all that I have seen amounts to little more than some slight fin injuries. But in comparison with the other Betta species it cannot be denied that these fish do possess a bit of a temperament. Nor could they be described as retiring and are generally "up front" in their activities around the aquarium.

Unfortunately breeding them is not without its problems. One of the prime concerns is the choice of two compatible partners. My observations lead me to conclude that only few of the males are inclined to spawn and rear the young. Courtship and spawning almost always takes place in the upper part of the second third of water, in the shelter of a group of plants. Practically all the initiative is taken by the female. After several "trial runs" the first actual acts of spawning take place. For this the female swims into a curve in the male's body, whereupon he will grip her and turn her on her back — a position that is adopted almost exclusively by bubble nest builders. This grappling lasts for about 2—3 seconds during which time the two fish sink through the water a little. After this the male releases the female and she will remain in a kind of "spawning stupor" (or rigor) for around 7 to 9 seconds before reawakening. After separation the female sinks to the bottom and on reaching it she is almost always in a vertical position, head down. The small number of eggs — there are usually one to three of them, largish, yellowish in colour — are picked up in the male's mouth once the female discharges them. He has also been seen to pick them up from the female's body, near the belly or anal zone. If he does not do so, they will loosen as the female starts to move on wakening from her spawning stupor. And as the female at this point is standing head down the eggs will fall to the bottom directly next to her head. She will then pick them up in her mouth and take them back to the spawning ground higher up and spit them out, whereupon the male will immediately take them into his mouth.

A direct "hand over" by this regurgitative method, as seen in most of the mouth brooding Betta species, has not been seen. On a number of occasions I had the impression that the female wanted to deposit the eggs she had picked up under a leaf in the spawning area, as if there were a bubble nest there. Between bouts of spawning the pair defends its spawning territory against other individuals of the same species. At a water temperature of 26 °C the hatching time is in the order of 8 days. The males then release between 20 and 45 youngsters around 6 mm long that immediately take freshly hatched *Artemia salina* as their first meal. So long as they have good quality water and a varied diet, the offspring are very fast growing and can reach a length of 3 cm after 6 weeks.

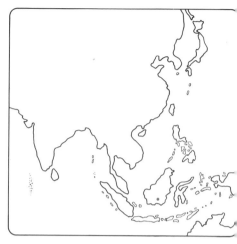

Asiatic distribution of *Betta spec. affin. foerschi.*

Betta spec. affin. foerschi.

Based on some important information we received from Father Heinz STROH MSF we were able to track down in July 1990 the very interesting species

▶ Beta spec. affin. patodi
from Pulau Laut

These fish belong unambiguously to the "macrostoma unimaculata group" and are also mouth brooding fighting fish. When fully adult they reach a total length of around 10 cm, it seems, and in comparison to *Betta unimaculata,* are much more colourful. With the current state of knowledge sexual differentiation is still difficult. It is possible that the females of this species are lacking colouring on the head and body parts. Overall they are less colourful and exhibit a dark longitudinal stripe, a feature which is shared by non dominant males. However, a characteristic typical of the species appears to be a white to light blue spot on the lower lip. It is a very "highly strung" fish and a good "leaper". Its natural habitat is found amongst the sometimes fast flowing mountain streams of the Gunung Sepatung mountain, south east of Kota Baru, the largest town on Pulau Laut, that is the island of Laut in the south east of South Kalimantan (Kalimantan Selatan). We found

Asiatic distribution of *Betta spec. affin. patodi.*

these fish in the streams and storage pools of the old Dutch water distribution networks. These were in parts very narrow, shallow watercourses with a large number of large and small rocks. The surrounding mountain jungle cast a shade over this biotope. The flowing water was very clear and colourless, with a general hardness of 2 and a carbonate hardness of 4. The electrical conductivity was 82 microsiemens at a temperature of 24.5 °C and pH value of 7.5.

Betta spec. affin. patodi.

A species that it has not been possible to classify hitherto is

▶ *Betta spec. affin. pugnax*

Odd specimens of this fish have reached our aquaria via the trade without our knowing very much about their origin or natural habitat. I first acquired this *Betta pugnax*-like species in 1979, it having been imported by the firm of Spree Aquarium-B. u. U. Borgwardt from Singapore. In comparison these fish are more colourful, with the males exhibiting green coloured gill covers and a more intensive body colour. But what distinguishes them above all from *B. pugnax* are the very much longer growing ventral fins which in their flattened position can almost reach down to the caudal peduncle. The females also have a comparatively slimmer and more pointed head i.e. one that is not so powerfully built. On this there is almost always a bold, dark longitudinal stripe that runs from the tip of the mouth through the eye to the edge of the gill cover. Investigations into the reproductive behaviour have not revealed any marked distinctive features during the mating phases but the brood development was indeed interesting. Whereas the embryos of *B. spec.* left

Presumed distribution of *Betta spec. affin. pugnax* in Asia.

the eggs after 58 hours, at similar temperatures the same process only took place in *B. pugnax* after 156 hours which is to say 4 days later. However, free swimming of the fully developed young was observed at a convergent time, after about 10 days and 12 hours.

Betta spec. affin. pugnax.

A hitherto unknown and still not classified species of fighting fish that we shall refer to here as

▶ Betta spec.
from Kubu

was discovered by us in 1990 to the south of the town of Pangkalanbun, just before the village of Kubu in Central Kalimantan (Kalimantan Tengah). The fish concerned was a single specimen with a total length of some 5 cm that was preserved on the spot. The outstanding features of this new species are its comparatively pointed head and its big eyes. As the photograph taken in the field shows, its colouring is very interesting.

The habitat in which this species was found was a little blackwater river with clear, gently flowing, very soft and very acidic water. General and carbonate hardness levels were both under 1. The pH value was 5.0 and the electrical conductivity was

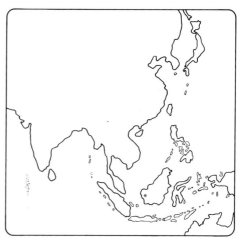

Asiatic distribution of *Betta spec.* from Kubu.

measured at 14 microsiemens at a water temperature of 23.7 °C.

Betta spec. from Kubu.

55

Another species that could possibly belong to the "foerschi-strohi group" originates from the Kapuas area and will be referred to here as

▶ *Betta spec.*
from Mandor

These fish reach a total length of around 55 mm. Their external appearance is reminiscent of *Betta splendens* and in comparison to *Betta strohi* and *Betta foerschi* they seem rather higher backed. A feature that seems to be characteristic of the males of the species is a laciniate or radiate extension to the middle of the caudal fin. Female specimens do not have this fin shape or at least only have a hint of it.

We found this fish in two separate localities. The first was on the road between Sungei Penjuh and Anjungan and the second just before Mandor which lies 20 km to the east. I consider the specimens found in both places to be the same species. One male taken at the Mandor locality released fry at a viable stage of development from his mouth shortly after we caught him. Accordingly, we take the species to be mouth brooders as well. In contrast to the first biotope, the fish

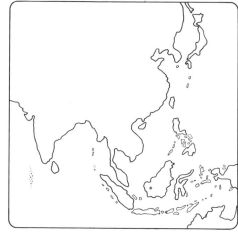

Asiatic distribution of *Betta spec.* from Mandor.

here were very numerous. The fish were living in a natural habitat that one could class as a typical blackwater environment. The water here was gently flowing, clear, dark brown coloured, very soft and very acidic. The general and carbonate hardness were both under 1 with a pH between 4.5 and 5.3. In August 1990 the temperature was measured at 27.6 and 28.2 °C.

Betta spec. from Mandor.

A further interesting species of fighting fish that Ingrid BAER, Norbert NEUGE-BAUER and the author were able to bring back from the 1990 expedition to Kaliman-tan will be referred to here after the site where it was found, namely

▶ *Betta spec.*
from Sanggau.

These fish seemingly attain an adult total length of 8 cm. The body colour of the males is a light, reddish brown. The scales on the sides of the body are covered in flecks of a light green shade. The mostly reddish brown fins are also flecked with light green. The gill covers are washed with dark green and the anal fin has a dark, almost black, hem. The species is very probably a mouth brooder. We do not yet have any observa-tions to hand on their reproductive biology.

Its habitat is located west of the town of Sanggau, south of the road from Pontianak to Sintang, about 7 km before Sanggau in a hilly bush and forest landscape behind the

Asiatic distribution of *Betta spec.* from Sanggau.

Monument to Fallen Patriots. These fish should be kept in soft, slightly acidic water. It seems that good water quality is import-ant if they are to feel at ease and do well.

Betta spec. from Sanggau.

A species that should also be counted amongst the "foerschi-strohi group", referred to here as

▶ Betta spec.
from Tarantang

was discovered during our expedition to Kalimantan in 1990. These fish attain a total length of about 6 cm. They display quite noticeable parallels to *Betta strohi* with which they share their habitat in places. But there are also some marked differences in their appearance. One particularly notice-able feature are the dark sports in the fins, the most striking of these being the one on the caudal fin. Unfortunately, only one spe-cimen found its way into our net which rather limits our attempts at further obser-vations and accurate classification.

The

natural habitat

of *Betta spec.* from Tarantang lies about 7 km south of Sukamara on the outskirts of the village of Tarantang in the south west of Central Kalimantan. It is a small stream that

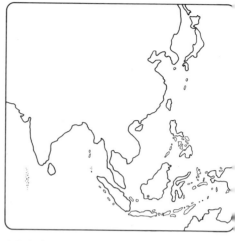

Asiatic distribution of *Betta spec.* from Tarantang.

skirts a washing and bathing place as it comes out of the forest. It carries a slightly brownish, clear, gently flowing water. It is very soft and low in minerals. The electrical conductivity was measured at 5 microsie-mens at a water temperature of 25.3 °C with a pH of 4.15.

Betta spec. from Tarantang.

The most beautiful and gloriously coloured of the labyrinth fish are

▶ *Betta splendens*
(REGAN, 1909)

the Siamese fighting fish

whose history, behaviour and present day significance in the lives of some of the peoples of Asia are well documented.

For centuries these fish have captivated people in Thailand and beyond. Contests between "Pla-Kat" — the biting and tearing fish — are still organised today, despite an official ban. In many a case they have altered the course of the life of certain individuals when a fortune could rest on the outcome of a fight, betting being the avid passion of many Asians.

The wild form of *Betta splendens* has long since been selectively bred to bring out more and more aggressive traits and fighting

spirit. If one puts two more or less equally sized males together, a fight will inevitably ensue. When they encounter each other in their natural habitat, the established territorial behaviour and the prevailing sexual mood of the individuals plays a major role. Here, after the appropriate displays of dominance and submission, the potential conflict will be resolved by the flight of one or other of them. But in a restricted space and with both parties stimulated to an equal degree, a merciless battle will develop, falling into several phases. The first phase involves displays of dominant poses, spreading of gill covers and bracing of fins. In the second phase currents of water are directed at the rival through hefty swipes of the tail. Then the first bouts of butting to body and fins introduces the close combat phase. In between there are continual spells of dominance poses. The third phase of the contest

Betta splendens, wild form.

unleashes biting and tearing attacks, above all to the sensitive gill and eye areas. The fish circle each other warily, looking for the most opportune time to inflict a shot at the head region, and all interspersed with blows delivered as direct physical attacks or as "water cannons". Phase four means reciprocal mouth-to-mouth tussles with the contestant that is on top trying to force his opponent to the bottom for the longest possible time, thereby depriving him from any access to atmospheric air. As the latter is vitally important to the fish, this phase of the fight is the most strength-sapping and likely to prove decisive. An alternating pattern of phases three and four brings the duel to a conclusion. A battle may last for hours and it is not always the injuries that decide

For breeding purposes the Thais put their stock into small ceramic containers.

Thai breeders line up jars in thousands for rearing Siamese fighting fish.

Any visitor to Thailand wanting to see fighting fish is soon accommodated by the local children.

the matter, for the fish often die from exhaustion. However, it is not the fighting aspect but the sheer pleasure of keeping and breeding this species that the amateur fishkeeper finds interesting.

The
natural habitat
In my opinion, the actual distribution range is very much smaller than had been supposed until now and is, in fact, restricted to central, western and northern Thailand, the latter being questionable too. *Betta splendens* lives in paddy fields and associated ditches, in marshes and flooded grass pits and in the klongs (canals) of the residential parts of towns and villages. At different times of the year they may be very numerous. However, when we talk about fighting fish these days, the fish in question is usually exclusively the veiled variety of *Betta splendens*. Its various colour sports and the hybrids with pointed, split, round, comb or fan tail, sometimes with a very broad dorsal fin, can be seen in practically all petshops and aquarium fish stockists throughout the world. The actual, pugnacious, short-finned wild form is only to be found in the tanks of really dedicated nature enthusiasts. Unfortunately, selective breeding of the veiled form on a massive scale aimed at producing yet more colour variants has led to the loss

Betta splendens, veiled form.

of the fighting instinct and quite often the great draped fins simply turn these fish into "worn out warriors". The over excitement of individual males while they are being raised in isolation in small glasses until they have grown into fine, mature specimens, leading to constant displaying — which in the view of the breeders induces especially long-finned individuals — in fact leads to a great waste of energy and reduced vitality.

Often the fish swimming around in aquaria are merely the "halt and the lame" but in spite of this they still count amongst the most popular ornamental fish of our day. Sexual differentiation is possible from a very early age. Whereas the females retain their short fins and, on reaching sexual maturity, usually at a length of 4 cm, exhibit a white spot, the protruding genital papilla just behind the ventral fins, the fins of the males grow much longer. This difference is especially easy to recognize on the dorsal fin that lengthens at a very early age and on the anal fin which extends a long way back.

Betta splendens. Various colour morphs of veiled Siamese fighting fish.

Asiatic distribution of *Betta splendens* (wild form only).

The mutual threat display is not an early distinguishing characteristic as it can be seen in both males and females. Young males should be kept apart from an early age because any fin injuries will only rarely grow out properly. Youngsters that are raised in large containers rather than small glasses are much more vital in constitution and much better suited as breeding stock. Males who grow up in the company of several members of the same species can be kept together for a long time in large tanks without any serious skirmishes taking place. It is only when "strangers" are put in or if they are removed from their community for a time that losses may occur.

No
natural habitat
as such exists for these veiled fighting fish.

Veiled Siamese fighting fish are the produce of Thai breeders, although one presumes that the first long-finned specimens came from the neighbouring country of Cambodia. At the end of the twenties they were starting to be imported into Germany and nowadays an aquarium without them would be almost unthinkable. In their home country too, they are part of the everyday scene. If you visit Bangkok today, any request for Siamese fighting fish will quickly be fulfilled. It will be the veiled form you see, an item that is bred in the hundreds of thousands as an export article to thrill people far away from their original home in south east Asia.

The
general care
of *Betta splendens* is unproblematical. They can be kept in either the "small" or the "large" aquarium for labyrinth fish. However, these fish are seen to best advantage in a smaller tank 70 cm long by 40 cm wide and about 30 cm high containing plenty of plants in parts. Several groups of tall stemmed plants like *Hygrophila stricta* and *Limnophila acquatica*, say 5 to 10 in total, should alternate with *Alternanthera sessilis* to form the main planting scheme at the rear of the aquarium and between these there should be some bogwood for decorative effect. In the foreground you could place two or three *Barclaya longifolia* and several *Cryptocoryne walkeri*. On the right and left hand sides plant eight stems of *Rotala macranda* to complete the overall picture. Leave some areas free between these plants so as to allow the fish some free swimming room.

Gravel with a grain size of 1 to 3 mm is recommended for the bed. Two or three floating plants such as *Ceratopteris pteridoides* and *Riccia flutans* can act as surface cover. The water temperature should be around 25 to 27 °C with a good filtration system like a Brillant internal filter to take care of clean, healthy water conditions. The water values are of lesser importance.

Almost any placid fish are recommended as companions except for various kinds of characins and barbs who often have the unfortunate habit of nibbling at the long fins of these fighting fish, thus causing unpleasant wounds. The aquarium should be well illuminated at 0.5 Watts per liter of water. Sufficient light is essential for healthy plant growth and with hard to medium hard water. Additions of carbon dioxide via a Tetra diffusion tube will prove beneficial. Following the maxim that healthy plant growth means healthy water, this will be reflected in the overall condition of the fish.

The view that fighting fish often live in mudholes and therefore can be kept in such conditions is not really tenable. The fish will exhibit their full finery in a well established, balanced aquarium and it is only under such conditions that their keeper will be able to appreciate their beauty at its best.

We now come to the

breeding

of these fish. For this you can use relatively small aquaria around 40 cm long, 30 cm wide and 20 cm high. They should be well planted with a number of floating plants shading the surface. A Brillant-Filter will guarantee sound water without causing excessive movement. The breeding tank needs to be well covered with a pane of glass so that the air above the water surface does not cool down too sharply, though this applies to other species of labyrinth fish too, given that they are all "fresh air breathers" and a temperature drop is bad for their health. Moreover, they are often good jumpers and quite capable of leaping out of the tank otherwise. For breeding, the temperature is raised to 30 °C and the tank is lit in the normal fashion.

For breeding, only one pair should be put in the above aquarium. As the males can be described at very least as "passionate" and accompany their attentions at the start with some outright aggression, you should

Spawning pair of *Betta splendens*, wild form.

ensure that any females used for this purpose are "in season". Such females can be recognised by their swollen girth. You should also test their willingness to mate and this can be done by placing the female in a part of the tank that has been partitioned off with a pane of glass or alternatively the female can be suspended in the breeding tank in a glass jar. The reaction of the female to the urgent attentions of the male gives an accurate indication of her willingness to mate. If she takes refuge amongst the plants or dashes back and forth fearfully, evidently seeking an escape route out of the jar, then you have to allow the two partners a lot more time to get used to each other behind the protective screen. However, if the female starts to exhibit a yellowish cross-striped pattern on a highly coloured body and swims towards the male with snakelike movements and head tilted slightly downwards, this is a clear sign of her willingness to mate. All the same, there may still be a good deal of hectic chasing around.

The male then starts building a bubble nest under or between the floating plants and usually the female will follow him there after just a short time, in response to his continuing advances. A number of "dummy runs" may precede the actual egg laying procedure which takes place after the usual intertwining, with the eggs falling on to the anal fin of the male. Once the eggs have emerged the male disentangles himself from the female and the eggs fall down through the water. The female will remain in the customary spawning stupor on the surface for a few seconds. During this time the male collects the falling eggs in his mouth, coats them in saliva and carefully spits them into the bubble nest, a procedure that the female will also participate in once she reawakens. The female will have deposited all her eggs after about two hours whereupon she will be driven away by the male who will undertake the care of the brood alone.

If there are enough hiding places available in the breeding tank, the female should not be removed because her presence causes the male to take better, more intensive care of the brood. However, both of them

should be removed after about four days when all the young are free swimming. Their very tiny offspring will then hold up just under the water surface or amongst the plants, on the lookout for something to eat. The recommended food for them is Tetra MikroMin which should be scattered on the surface in small amounts several times a day. An extra airstone hung in the tank will ensure the water movement needed to distribute the food. On this good diet the youngsters will grow well and can be given additional nauplii of the brine shrimp, *Artemia salina*. After about ten days, instead of the powdered food Tetra MikroMin which is now reduced to two feeds a day, you should give them the growth promoting flaked food TetraOvin. The high rate of metabolic processes going on in the tank resulting from the rapid growth of the fry, means that the waste products produced can no longer be dealt with even by the plants and the high performance Brillant Filter. Consequently, it is absolutely essential that one third of the water be changed every three to five days and that the filter cartridge be cleaned every two days. With such tender loving care these little chaps will grow up into magnificent specimens. The sexes can be differentiated after just two to three months and at four to five months old they too are capable of breeding. But important factors in the whole of this procedure are due attention to water quality and, above all, the right food because any mistakes made in the first days of their life cannot be rectified. The procedure described above should be regarded as the norm.

Unfortunately, with these overbred or inbred veiled forms of Siamese fighting fish, frequent mismatches occur, with poor fertilization and excessively aggressive behaviour of the males. By the same token, their brood care behaviour is often very deficient or totally absent. Specimens that display this tendency should be weeded out and not used for breeding purposes. Usually, individuals that have grown up in containers with plenty of swimming room will give more harmonious and successful results as breeding stock than "jam jar" specimens.

Egg development of *Betta splendens*, wild form, observed at a water temperature of 26 °C.

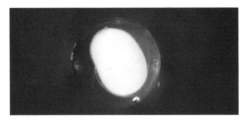

2 hours after fertilization the first signs of development are seen. Cell division is apparent.

4 hours after fertilization distinct cleavage is seen.

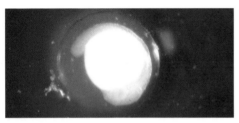

23 hours after fertilization. Rudimentary embryo in the form of a head and embryonic stick are seen.

32 hours after fertilization. Embryo easily visible. Embryonic stick detached from yolk. Intermittent movements of the egg sac.

44 hours after fertilization. Larvae hatched, 26 mm long. Eye cleavage and vertebral column visible.

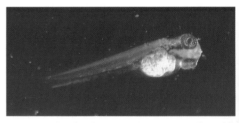

58 hours after fertilization. Eyes, anus and mouth easily visible.

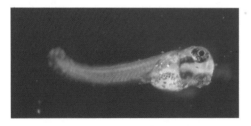

68 hours after fertilization. Good protective marking. All bodily parts functioning. Eyes, mouth and gills formed. Pectoral fins active.

12 hours before free swimming. Young fish fully developed. Yolk almost consumed. Development completed after 3 days and 20 hours.

At the start of 1990 a new, very beautiful species of fighting fish belonging to the "foerschi-strohi group" was described and has been named as

◆ *Betta strohi*
(SCHALLER and KOTTELAT, 1990)

Named after its collector, Peter Heinz STROH MSF, who lived for many years in Kalimantan, carrying out intensive ich-thyological research. Without question *Betta strohi* shows a very close relationship to *Betta foerschi*. Nevertheless, as SCHAL-LER and KOTTELAT state in their first description, there are also marked morho-logical distinguishing features. A noticeable feature is perhaps the extended central part of the caudal fin that grows out to a pointed tip. The females too exhibit a divergent pat-terning in their courtship display colouring. In this, very dark coloured cross stripes can be seen over the body and these extend as far as the anal fin. The fish brought back by us — which grow to about 6.5 cm long — originate from the Nataisedawak area, about

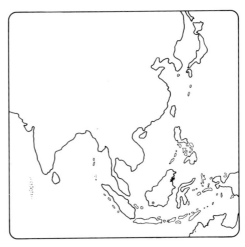

Asiatic distribution of *Betta strohi*.

4 km south of Sukamara in the south west of Central Kalimantan. We identified speci-mens of the fish in the headwaters and springs of the area. Nothing is yet known about the reproductive biology of this species. We presume it to be a mouth brooder.

Betta strohi.

One of the less well known and rarely kept species of *Betta* is

▶ *Betta taeniata*
(REGAN, 1909)

a peaceable species of fighting fish that grows to 8 cm in length.

It is not difficult to separate the two sexes as there are certain clear distinguishing features. As the males are often prone to taking on the longitudinal patterning of the females — which also serves as alarm signal — a clear differentiation is only difficult in young specimens. The fins are usually coloured deep green with the anal fin having a dark, usually blue egde.

The

natural habitat
is reckoned to be Sumatra, Borneo, Malaysia and Thailand. The extent to which there is a connection with *Betta pugnax* has not yet been completely cleared up.

I caught some of them in a watercourse around Kampang Matang in the vicinity of Kuching, the capital of Sarawak. The fish

Betta taeniata.

kept mainly to the areas of calm water near to the banks and the associated vegetation. The water was flowing and a deep brownish colour.

Table No. 3

Locality:	Watercourse in the area of Kampong Matang, near Kuching in Sarawak
Clarity:	clear
Colour:	dark brown
pH value:	5.5
D general hardness	under 1 °dH
D carbonate hardness	under 1 °dH
Conductivity:	6 microsiemens at 26.5 °C
Nitrite:	0.05 mg/l
Water depth:	up to 1 m
Water movement:	little
Water temperature:	26.5 °C
Date of tests:	12. 3. 1980
Time:	12.00

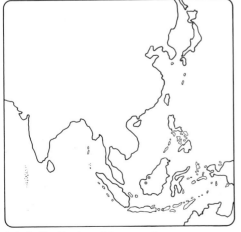

Asiatic distribution of *Betta taeniata*.

The
general care
of this species is not difficult. Their aquarium should not be too small and the water values should be in the soft range. Good peat filtration of the water over peat fibre should be provided together with additional aeration. Plenty of plants, as well as two or three cavities made of stones or coconut shells are highly recommended. Large-leaved species of plants should be borne in mind as these fish like to pass the time under their shade, enjoying the shelter from the water surface. As material for the bed, gravel with a grain size between 1 and 3 mm should be used. Normal lighting, i.e. 0.5 Watts per liter, will suffice. The water temperature should be a 24 °C with regular water changes, replacing a quarter to a third of the contents every fortnight, being advisable. Good, high grade food is required. They have a liking for TetraMin. The aquarium should be located in a quiet position as this species is somewhat shy.

Breeding
successes in this species have been few and far between. Walter ARMBRUST from Hamburg has been able to observe their spawning procedures closely but, like me, has not had any success in raising the fry. If you want to give it a shot, you should use an aquarium set up in the same way as for normal care, with the temperature raised to 27 °C. The water values should be adapted to reflect those found in the natural habitat. As the few fish that occasionally reach us are exclusively wild caught specimens, it is probable that development of the eggs is only possible in water that has values similar to those found in their natural biotope. At spawning time the males are light grey to a delicate green, with greenish white tips to the scales. The females exhibit a light longitudinal stripe and the rest of the body has a dark grey hue. Mating takes place generally under a large leaf or an overhanging rock, just a few centimeters above the bed. This spawning ground is fearlessly defended, above all by the female. Other fish are driven

from the scene. Spawning is preceded by several trial runs, with the female swimming around the slightly bent male and touching him lightly with her mouth on the middle of his body, level with his dorsal fin. At this point the male will wrap himself around the female in a brief embrace, forming a U-shape with his head and tail uppermost. This coupling lasts about 5 seconds before the pair separate again. The female takes the eggs that have been deposited on to the anal fin of the male into her mouth. It is only after several minutes, during which she appears to "chew over" the batch of eggs, that she spits them one by one in front of the male's mouth. If he fails to catch any of them — which happens quite often at the start of proceedings — she gathers them up again. At times it seems as if a game of catch is developing. Renewed spawning only takes place once all the eggs of the previous phase, some 5 to 15 in all, have been accepted by the male. From time to time they will take a break to defend their territory, with the female being the more active of the two in this activity as well. "Phantom" matings continue to take place throughout the entire act of spawning, with the individual egg laying phases occurring at intervals of 10 to 20 minutes. The whole process takes about six hours.

Afterwards, when the male has taken over all the eggs, he will retire to a quiet, sheltered part of the aquarium. Here, with raised gill covers and occasional chewing motions, he takes care of his brood while the female defends him for a time.

The fry emerge from their "den" after about ten days of development and grow relatively quickly. It seems that the parents do not molest their young but a plentiful amount of cover in the form of floating plants is still advisable to provide the fry with a refuge in an emergency.

A watercourse in the region of Matang, the habitat of *Betta taeniata*.

A new species of fighting fish that shows similarities to *Betta coccina* is

▶ *Betta tussyae*
(SCHALLER, 1985)

This species is a small bubble nesting type that reaches a total length of around 6 cm in the aquarium. Sexual differentiation is not always easy. The dorsal, anal and ventral fins of the males grow rather longer and they appear to be more deeply coloured than the females. In the wild their range is restricted to the area around the town of Kuantan on the east coast of the Malaysian peninsula. The species lives here in the same habitats as *Sphaerichthys o. osphremenoides, Parosphro-menus nagyi* and occasionally *Betta imbellis*. These biotopes are usually small streams and shallow, gently flowing accumulations of water that in the drought period are only a few centimetres deep. Here the fish live amongst dead leaves and dense clumps of aquatic plants. René KRUMMENACHER (1985), who found this species in several localities in this area, made the following notes: "Kuantan Segamat road, 3.6 km before Kuantan, right hand side of the road. Water pH 5.5, 15 microsiemens, tea-coloured water, 0.2 – 2 m wide and 0.5 – 2 m deep, gently flowing to still."

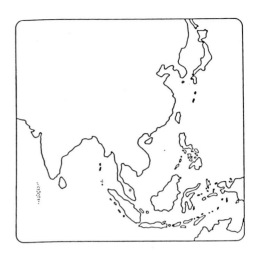

Asiatic distribution of *Betta tussyae*.

Based on our experience to date it is recommended that they be kept in clean, acidic water with a low mineral content and a pH value around 5 at a temperature between 25 and 27 °C.

The information given by KRUMME-NACHER and WASER was gathered in the low water months of July and August. So the results of my research conducted in January 1987, that is at the height of the rainy season with good water levels, could

Betta tussyae.

71

represent an interesting comparison. There is a little river about 8 m wide with broad curves up to 20 m across that passes under the Kuantan-Mersing-Johor Baharu highway between the 16 to 17 km to Kuantan "milestone" (alternatively the 313 to 312 to Johor Baharu "milestone") through a 12 m long concrete bridge. In parts it flows through areas of dense low-growing forest which, however, only offers little in the way of shade. The water is very clear and deep brown colour. In mid channel there is a strong current. In the numerous little hollows cut into the bank by erosion there is an astonishing number of *Betta tussyae* and above all *Parosphromenus nagyi*. This meant that in about half an hour I was able to catch around 30 of the latter from amongst the dead leaves and emergent vegetation of these 20 to 40 cm deep hollows. These had an average length of two to three centimeters. *Betta tussyae* were also relatively common here, the individuals present being up to two or three centimeters long. Other species present in this habitat include *Sphaerichthys o. osphromenoides*, *Betta pugnax, snake-heads* and *Trichogaster vittatus*.

The water in these hollows is almost stagnant and has a temperature of 23.9 °C. The pH value is around 3.62 but falls to as low as 3.28 in the stagnant zones with lots of vegetation and dead leaves. The electrical conductivity is 49 microsiemens (pH 3.62). The general and carbonate hardness levels are under 1 ° dH. The water is subjected to the full force of the sun's rays for most of the day. The tests were carried out at around 14.30.

It is interesting to note that there was a relatively high population density of juvenile specimens of *Betta tussyae* and largish *P. nagyi* per square meter. A trawl with the hand net very close to the bank would bring in anything from one to five specimens of these species. They were always to be found amongst dense plant growth, debris and suchlike in the shallow water in these bank areas. The deep brown colour of the water was amazing and can probably be attributed to the sheer quantity of leaves dumped in the water by the surrounding trees. The bed consisted of a reddish brown sandy material with good levels of loam and laterite. Though a very "rich mixture", there were no aquatic plants in the main river.

A *Betta tussyae* biotope about 16 km south of Kuantan.

A fish that belongs in the "macrostoma-patodi-unimaculata" group is

▶ *Betta unimaculata*
(POPTA, 1905)

This is without doubt one of the most magnificently coloured of the mouth brooding *Betta* species and can grow to a total length of up to 12 cm. It is possible to differentiate between the sexes when they are half grown. The males are more intensely coloured, have a large head and are endowed with a deep green coloured gill cover plate. This species needs a high grade diet and is generally very peaceable towards other fish, including smaller species.

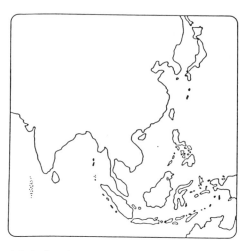

Asiatic distribution of *Betta unimaculata*.

In terms of

general care
this species is trouble-free and is not at all fussy in respect of the water quality it requires. All the same, it should be pointed out that these are not fish for very soft water, especially if it is very acidic.

Nor is their

breeding
a great problem, with the requirements and procedures involved being somewhat similar to those for *Betta pugnax*. Whereas in almost all species of mouth brooding Bettas it is the female who picks up the eggs in her mouth after fertilization, handing them over to the male by spitting them in front of him for him to brood in his mouth, in *Betta unimaculata* the male picks up the eggs himself immediately. In this case the female does not intervene and so there is none of the otherwise characteristic "interplay" between the pair. At a water temperature of 25 °C the male's "brooding" duties take about 15 days, at which point the ca. 7 mm long fry leave the safe haven of their father's mouth. They immediately take newly hatched nauplii of *Artemia salina* as their first meal. Once they

Betta unimaculata, wild form.

have left their father's care there is no further bond between parent and offspring but he does not inflict any unwelcome attentions on them either. If they are given a high grade, varied diet and have good, proper water conditions in their breeding tank, the young fish will grow very quickly. At around two months old young *Betta unimaculata* can already be about 5 cm long. The average number of young in a given brood is between 50 and 80.

The
natural habitat
is found in the south of Sabah on the island of Borneo (East Malaysia). I was able to verify the presence of this species in the areas around Tawau in 1980. This is a town on the Celebes Sea near to the border with the Indonesian part of the island of Borneo, Kalimantan. The landscape surrounding Tawau comprises almost exclusively oil palm, rubber and cocoa plantations and consequently, the watercourses are all influenced by human management. The large quantities of insecticides deposited here by crop spraying programmes fortunately does not appear to have affected the underwater flora and fauna. As the watercourses all have some form of flowing current in them a constant exchange of water

takes place and the frequent falls of rain accelerate this process. *Betta unimaculata* is abundant in this area. They lead a retiring solitary existence, concealed amongst plants and weeds in the water margins. The individuals found here were often medium sized specimens with total lengths up to 9 cm. In the side arms of these generally two to three meters wide waterways you can frequently come across young fish up to 3 cm long often living amongst the fallen leaves in water only 2 cm deep.

Mention should also be made of the findings relating to the water quality in this area as they are important for successful breeding. Twelve miles north of Tawau I measured the following values at 11.00 on 21. 3. 1980 in a watercourse about 3 meters wide: general and carbonate hardness, about 4 °dH; pH value 7.5; conductivity 80 microsiemens; all measured at a water temperature of 25 °C. I was also able to investigate a second biotope around 25 km east of the town of Tawan on the Balung River. Here too the landscape is dominated by oil palm and cocoa plantations. I did not find any of these fish in the river itself but the adjacent, gently flowing water channels in the plantations contained an abundance of them. The water values here were almost identical to those above.

Betta unimaculata, hybrid form, "The blue unimaculata".

A group of very undemanding, easily kept, yet very colourful labyrinth fish are the slimline, high backed species of the genus *Colisa*. Their range covers the whole of India and up into Burma.

One of the smallest representatives of this genus is the very vivid species, occasionally referred to as *Colisa sota*, but more properly called

▶ *Colisa chuna*
(HAMILTON-BUCHEMANN, 1822)

and known by the common English name of honey gourami. It attains a total length of up to 5 cm. In the adult state the males acquire a luminous orange red hue over most of their body, including the caudal fin. The gill areas below the eyes, the abdomen, the lower part of the belly and the hard ray section of the anal fin are coloured dark blue to almost black. The hard ray section up to the upper part of the soft rays of the dorsal fin is a lemon-yellow shade. The females are a uniform grey with a single, dark brown

Colisa chuna, wild form.

longitudinal stripe that turns pale at times. Unfortunately, submissive or frightened males also display this female coloration and this can lead to some difficulties in differentiating the sexes. Females that are ready to mate can be recognised by the swollen appearance of their abdomen region.

The
natural habitat
has been described by the ichthyologist Francis DAY as the Assam valley, the great floodplain of the Bramaputra River in the north east of India, extending to the floodplain and delta of the Ganges (Ganga) and Jamuna in what is now Bangladesh and then on to the Hugli (Hooghly) River, west of the line from Krishnagar to Calcutta.

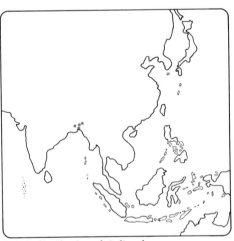

Asiatic distribution of *Colisa chuna.*

The
general care
of the honey gourami requires little more than the specification outlined in the section on the "small aquarium for labyrinth fish", with a tank up from 50 cm long and 30 cm deep and wide being ideal.

Several clumps of plants comprising 5 to 10 *Hygrophila difformis* (synonymous with *Synema triflorum)* should be provided, the number depending on the size of the aquarium. Planted in a 2 to 3 cm deep bed of gra-

vel with grain diameter up to 3 mm, these should grow up to reach the surface.

A dark backdrop will provide an excellent contrast to these bright subjects and clear water with a light motion will enhance their wellbeing. No particular attention needs to be paid to the water values so long as it is not too rich in minerals or alkaline. These water values can be tested in just a matter of seconds by using the Tetra GH Test and Tetra KH Test as well as the Tetra pH Test kits. If the GH and KH values are above 15° dH, it is recommended that the water be filtered over active peat and for reducing the KH values (carbonate hardness), additional carbon dioxide is advisable as well as peat filtration. The simplest and safest method of achieving this is with the Tetra CO_2 diffusion tube, irrespective of the water values. The temperature should be about 25 °C and the level of lighting around 0.5 Watts per liter. Bogwood and caves and the usual floating plants are not a prerequisite for these species but can prove a nice optional extra.

For
breeding
Colisa chuna the details specified above should be followed but the water temperature ought to be raised to 28 − 30 °C and the water filtered via a Tetra Brillant Filter, as the wake from the equipment is not as fierce and presents less of a threat to the young fish.

A good cover for the aquarium by means of a pane of glass or other translucent material will prevent cooling the air above the water surface and stop the fish leaping out, a recommendation that applies to all labyrinth fish species.

Another very beautiful species of Colisa, which unfortunately only shows the full glory of its colours when it reaches adult size, is

▶ *Colisa fasciata*
(BLOCK and SCHNEIDER, 1801)

which comes from Bangladesh amongst other places and is known in English as the striped or banded gourami. It is something of a giant, reaching a length of 10 to 12 cm when fully grown, though admittedly a very gentle one. The coloration of the males is bright and attractive whilst the background colour of the females remains a rather sombre grey. Sadly, the distinctive colouring of the males takes its time in developing. This means that they are 5 to 6 cm long before it is possible to distinguish between the sexes. Males of this species have their dorsal fin extended into a point and edged with a white hem. Their anal fin has a similar pointed shape with a red rim to it.

Colisa fasciata.

Their

natural habitat

is the coastal lowlands of the Coromandel coast of the states of Tamil Nadu and Andhra Pradesh in south east India where the native population is very high so that much of the land is dedicated to rice growing. Furthermore, as in *Colisa chuna* and

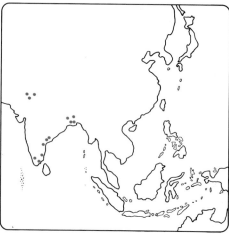

Asiatic distribution of *Colisa fasciata*.

Colisa lalia, the areas around Bengalen in north west India and Bangladesh are known habitats of this species.

Breeding

these fish is simple and unproblematical. As this species is somewhat larger than the rest of the Colisa genus, aquaria upwards of 100 cm long, 40 cm wide and 40 cm deep are recommended. Decoration should consist of various groups of plants, such as *Hygrophila difformis*, hitherto also known as *Synema triflorum*, or *Limnophila heterophylla*, together with single dot plants of *Ceratopteris pteridoides* to give a certain degree of surface cover.

For *Colisa fasicata* the parameters of the "small" or "large" aquarium for labyrinth fish could be considered appropriate.

The water temperature should lie between 23 and 25 °C and can only fluctuate by 1 to 2 °C over the day/night period. It is not demanding in respect of water quality and only requires normal lighting.

For

breeding

the chosen tank size should not be less than 100 cm long and 40 cm wide as these fish are very fecund and productive. With 20 cm of water in the tank several clumps of plants can be set out, comprising *Vallisneria spiralis*, the common eel grass, or *Hygrophila corymbosa*. Also recommended are a number of floating plants like *Pistia stratiotis*, also known as water salad, or *Riccia flutans*, crystalwort in English, though these are not taken into consideration by the male when it comes to selecting a site for his bubble nest.

The water temperature should be raised to 28 °C and a filtration system such as the Tetra Brillant Filter installed, because, with the large number of young fish you can expect, good water quality is going to be vital. Lighting can be rather more subdued than normal for the duration of the courtship but once spawning has successfully taken place, it can be brought back up to the normal level of about 0.5 Watts per liter so that the plants will have sufficient light thus guaranteeing healthy growth. Remember, if the plants are healthy then this indicates you are looking after the water in the right way. Even so, if you have a large number of fry in the tank you should change up to one third of the water every three to five days. Tetra MikroMin is very suitable as a first food as this is specially formulated to cater to the nutritional requirements of young fish. But as the appetite of baby *Colisa fasciata* is quite voracious, you can start putting them on to nauplii of *Artemia salina* after just 10 days.

A further species of *Colisa* for which the situation as to whether it is a species in its own right or just a colour or geographical variant of *Colisa fasciata* is still not clear, has been given the name

◆ Colisa labiosa
(DAY, 1878)

2.5"-3 1/4"

the thick-lipped gourami.

They are somewhat smaller and attain an adult total length of 6 to 8 cm. Here too the males are very beautifully coloured and have a pointed tip to their dorsal fin which in this case is edged with red. In *Colisa labiosa* the anal fin is rounded and has a white edge. The ground colour of the females is likewise grey.

The

natural habitat

was stated as Burma in DAY's original description, covering the Irrawaddy River in the north with the fertile plains of the provincial capital of Mandalay, down to the delta region of the Irrawaddy in the south with the capital Rangoon and the port of Bassein. The extent to which *Colisa labiosa* occurs in the locations mentioned by REGAN which were on average at elev-ations of 1000 meters in the Shan highlands in eastern Burma, has still to be checked out.

In contrast, they occur in plentiful numbers in Bangladesh, a new and as yet little known locality.

As the

general care and breeding

of *Colisa labiosa* and *Colisa fasciata* are identical, I refer the reader to the section on the former species.

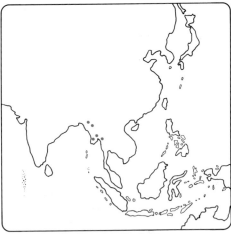

Asiatic distribution of *Colisa labiosa*.

Colisa labiosa.

Another species of *Colisa* and indeed one of the most popular and best known of the genus, is

▶ *Colisa lalia*
(HAMILTON-BUCHANAN, 1822)

2.5″

the dwarf gourami.

This is a small species, only reaching a length of 6 cm. The males exhibit their colourful attire at an early age whilst the females retain their silvery grey basic coloration. Likewise, while the soft rays of the dorsal fin on the males extend to a point, in the females these are a soft rounded shape. The

natural habitat

is described by Francis DAY as the lowlands of north east India and Bangladesh, including the delta and general catchment area of the rivers Ganges (Ganga) and Jumuna, as the Bramaputra is called in its delta region. *Colisa lalia* is often seen in the company of *Colisa chuna* and *Colisa fasciata* and, unsurprisingly, similar conditions apply to all three species.

For the

general care

of *Colisa lalia* an aquarium size upwards of 50 cm long, 30 cm wide and 30 cm deep will suffice. For this species the "small aquarium

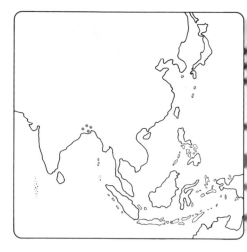

Asiatic distribution of *Colisa lalia*.

Colisa lalia, wild form.

80

Hybrid form of *Colisa lalia*, the "red lalia".

Hybrid form of *Colisa lalia*, the "rainbow lalia".

for labyrinth fish" is perfectly adequate. Included in the standard decoration of this tank you should always provide some bogwood and groups of plants such as *Limnophila aquatica* and *Hygrophila polysperma*, the Indian water star, in each case five to ten stems planted in fine gravel with a grain size of up to 3 mm. Some surface cover should be given by providing floating plants like *Riccia flutans*, the Crystalwort. Generally speaking it is possible to use tap water for these fish, provided that it is not too hard and alkaline. This can be easily verified by checking with the Tetra GH-Test, the Tetra KH-Test and the Tetra pH-Test. The normal temperature should be around 25 °C. The aquarium should be well lit and be placed in a quiet spot. You should avoid unnecessary disturbance to the aquarium and any knocking against its sides because *Colisa lalia* will react to this by becoming very withdrawn and timid.

An aquarium set up in this way is also quite suitable for the purpose of

breeding

All you need to do is to lower the water level to a depth of 10 to 15 cm and raise the temperature to 28 to 30 °C. It is also important to use a lot of aquatic plants like *Limnophila aquatica* and the floating plant *Riccia flutans*, because *Colisa lalia* males are master builders when it comes to constructing their bubble nests. Incorporating parts of the leaves of these plants, especially those floating on the surface, they fashion a structure bordering on a work of art, often up to 6 cm in diameter and protruding up to 2 cm out of the water.

Once a male *Colisa lalia* has completed the task of nest building, he will look for a female that is willing to mate. He courts her with outstretched fins and movements that are generally designed to impress the object of his affections, swimming around her and inviting her back to the nest. On arrival underneath the nest, the male commences swimming around his partner, displaying his finest colours. The female is not infrequently taken aback by the ardour of the male and may take fright and flee. But as the game is

likely to be repeated a few minutes later they will eventually come to accept one another and begin swimming in circles together. At a certain point the female will then touch the male in the belly or tail region with the tip of her mouth and this contact represents the trigger for the male to entwine himself around her. He wraps himself around her and pushes her on to her side and subsequently, after a few seconds on to her back. On doing so the eggs emerge and are immediately fertilized. After a few more seconds the fish release themselves from this embrace and the eggs are freed to float up to the surface. The female then leaves the spawning ground and the male collects the eggs in his mouth, taking them straight back to the nest. Only when all the eggs are gathered and secured in position with additional bubbles of air do they proceed with the next mating. If there are a number of females in the aquarium it is possible that the male could mate with various partners in a given session. After about two hours the male will take sole charge of the eggs.

The first embryos start to emerge from the egg shell after about 12 - 14 hours, given a water temperature of 27 °C. The larvae show a clear head shape after 24 hours and the embryonic stick begins to stand out as a vertebral column. In addition, the first sign of protective pigment can be seen on the body. After around 33 hours the eyes show up the gold and black iris which is clearly developed after 52 hours and is already capable of movement. Ten hours later, that is 62 hours after spawning, the larvae are showing good protective pigmentation over the entire body. The fins are fully recognisable. The yolk sac is completely consumed and the internal organs can be seen to be fully functional.

At this point, two days and 14 hours after spawning, the fry leave their father's nest swimming freely. Once the brood are free swimming, the parents should be removed from the breeding tank. Tetra MikroMin should then be given as their first food and an airstone hung in the aquarium and run at a moderate speed.

Hybrid form of *Colisa lalia*, the "neon lalia".

Hybrid form of *Colisa chuna*, the "yellow honey gourami".

A species that has as yet been little researched is

◗ *Ctenops nobilis*
(McCLELLAND, 1845)

This previously little imported species started to arrive in Europe in large numbers for the first time in the middle of 1986. Those few individuals that had been imported in 1912 and 1955/56 were insufficient to tell us very much about *Ctenops nobilis*. Even today little is known about their needs in terms of general care and breeding biology. The matter of sexual differentiation too is based on hearsay and assumptions. Experience to date tells us that *Ctenops nobilis* is a rather sensitive subject and somewhat tricky to keep. Nor are we quite sure whether this fish is a specialist feeder or not, seeing as they seem to fall between the genera *Sphaerichthys* and *Trichopsis*. In the aquarium the fish live in the upper water levels, preferring densely overgrown zones and those covered with floating plants. The current state of our knowledge indicates that these are not predatory fish. Their favourite food seems to consist of all types of insects and insect larvae, with black mosquito larvae apparently having particular appeal. Whether the long snout has any special significance for its feeding habits is not yet fully understood. As the species has

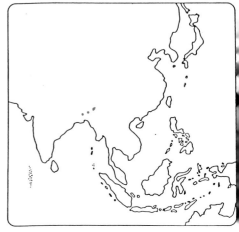

Asiatic distribution of *Ctenops nobilis*.

proved to be somewhat susceptible and "perishable" in captivity, it is not yet clear, given that they have all been wild caught specimens, whether these individuals had been damaged in transit or whether we are simply not yet capable of understanding the right way of keeping them. It is possible that they require subtropical conditions, that is somewhat cooler water temperatures.

Their

natural habitat
is found in eastern India and Bangladesh. Their range hitherto has been defined as the

Ctenops nobilis.

Assam region and the area surrounding Dacca. This was about all we knew about this species until recently. In January 1987 I wanted to find out some more precise details about them and came up with some rather interesting results.

My research began in Dacca and it has to be said that the Bangladeshi capital offers plenty of potential sources of information. These range from the countless fish markets, large and small, in all parts of the city, where a multitude of freshwater fish are on offer to the occasional aquarist shop and the Ichthyological Department of Dacca University. In addition there are also within very close range of Dacca a series of fish farms dedicated to raising fish commercially, and specialising for the most part in angel fish, livebearers and goldfish. Indigenous fish are only rarely stocked although you do come across *Colisa lalia* and *Colisa chuna* on sale occasionally. The vast array of popular aquarium fish to be found in the flat, watery landscape in the countryside in Bangladesh is indeed impressive, with the labyrinth fish well to the forefront. As well as the species already mentioned, namely *Colisa lalia* and *Colisa chuna*, there is also a great population of *Colisa labiosa* and *Colisa fasciata*, with *Colisa chuna* being more predominant in the south western part of the country. In many biotopes I was also able to confirm the presence of *Anabas oligolepis* and *A. testudineus*. In contrast, *Ctenops nobilis* is relatively rare and I was only able to find five of them, making them a very scarce commodity indeed compared with the other species. However as I soon found out, there were very good reasons for this. Whilst the other species of labyrinth fish listed here are also to be found in large numbers in plant-free water zones in which the fishermen can operate easily with their vast nets, *Ctenops nobilis* only lives in the uppermost strata of areas thick in aquatic and floating plants. This species seldom ventures into open or deeper waters. And as these areas are not attractive in terms of offering lucrative catches, *Ctenops nobilis* is a relatively rare commodity on the markets.
The general consensus seemed to be that this fish, like the *Colisa* species, is a bubble nest builder which builds a medium sized bubble nest amongst groups of floating plants and spawn beneath it. The males of *Ctenops nobilis*, which have a larger and longer dorsal fin and are more deeply coloured, take care of the brood. All these species spawn in March with the onset of the monsoon rains. At this time broad expanses of the land are flooded and the associated "thinning" of the water together with the sudden availability of tiny food items seem to be the trigger for the reproductive activity that starts then. About two months after the monsoon the general view seemed to be that *Ctenops nobilis* was again numerous.

The fish have a variety of local names, depending on the locality and may be known as *Modumala, Nakteceuda, Naktecolischa, Nagdani* and *Chibcilli*.

Generally speaking, they seem to occur in little ponds and shallow, standing stretches of streams and rivers where they occupy the upper water levels between clumps of plants. Above all, we were able to confirm their presence in the south western and western areas of Dacca down into the region around Calcutta. What is interesting though are the water compositions encountered in this range. These are usually soft to medium hard waters showing a reaction around neutral.

In January I measured the following water values in a stretch of water covered with water hyacinths near to Dhamrai; the exact point was on the road to Aricha on the Jamuna River where the Jamuna (Bramaputra) and Ganga converge. GH and KH were around 4 °dH and the pH 6.76 (measured by electronic means); the electrical conductivity was 182 microsiemens at 22.6 °C.

In the intervening period Sven BITSCH has succeeded in breeding this fish. According to his notes it is the female of the species that carried out the mouth brooding duties. After quite a lengthy brood period she released out of her mouth about 150 5–6 mm long fry which immediately started taking newly hatched Artemia as their first food. It is possible that this species is exclusively a mouth brooder.

One of the labyrinth fish that is considered as a great delicacy in its country of origin because of its great size is

▶ *Helostoma temminckii*
(CUVIER and VALENCIENNES, 1831)
the kissing gourami.

Two variants of this species are known, the silvery grey natural form and a flesh-coloured variant. In their natural habitat they are said to grow to a total length of 30 cm but in the large aquarium they only reach 15 to 20 cm.

It is very difficult to tell the sexes apart as there are no external features that give any sort of clue. Only in larger specimens about 12 cm long are there any discernible hints. Looked at from above the females seem to be broader and this appears to be the only possible distinction, apart from a larger breast and belly area at spawning time.

There is a further possibility for identifying males. For this the fish has to be removed from the water. It is held on its back in the hand. Very gentle, smooth massaging of the belly on both sides of the body will quickly cause the white sperm to appear in the genital zone of mature males. This is an interesting technique for sexing fish that has been practised by breeders in Thailand for some time.

Their
natural habitat
is Thailand, Malaysia, Borneo and Sumatra. The extent to which this fish has had its range extended through its use as a commercial species is difficult to assess. Broadly speaking, they live in major rivers, swamps and also in smaller, lake-sized accumulations of water. As they are in great demand as table fish they are raised specifically for this purpose in many places. Since a live fish commands a much better price on the markets in these hot, humid tropical zones than a dead one, this species, being an air

Helostoma temminckii, wild form.

breather, is much better adapted to with-standing the stress and rigours of transport to the consumer than a gill breathing fish. Moreover, a good-sized *Helostoma tem-minckii* tips the scales at about one kilo, making it a very interesting proposition for fishmonger and consumer alike.

The Thai fish farmers keep kissing gouramis in open air ponds about 8 × 15 m with a water depth of about 80 cm. In such conditions the temperature can quickly rise to 30 °C when the sun is shining. The high evaporation is evened out through well water during drought periods though this task is managed by nature in the rainy season. These fishponds are stocked with small fish, about 4 to 5 cm long, which will take about a year to attain a marketable size. Their feed consists of the strange combination of whatever the open air ponds have to offer naturally and fresh pig manure. The original pig food in its half-converted state and still containing a high proportion of

Asiatic distribution of *Helostoma temminckii*.

vegetable matter represents a very vitamin-rich diet. Whatever scraps remain uneaten then go into a sort of soup in which plankton will thrive, attracting insects to lay their

Helostoma temminckii, hybrid form.

Kissing gouramis about 20 cm long taken from open air breeding ponds in Thailand.

Plastic netting is suspended in the ponds to act as swimming enclosures for the kissing gouramis.

eggs which in time hatch out onto larvae. In spite of all this, the self regenerating capacity of the water is astonishing to behold and the rate at which the fish grow is equally amazing. Any specimens that are especially large and vigorous are selected for breeding. Before the pond is pumped dry to harvest the crop of kissing gouramis, a number of specimens are caught with the cast net for appraisal. Those that are suitable for breeding are sorted out and separated according to sex in plastic nets that are suspended in the ponds as two to three square meter floating cages.

For breeding they use round concrete containers with a diameter of about 80 cm. These are cleaned thoroughly and then filled with fresh water to adept of around 40 cm. Into this they put one pair of *Helostoma temminckii*. Where the female has a good build up of spawn as an enforced consequence of the separation of the sexes earlier, they will mate after just a couple of hours. The eggs emerge as the partners embrace and rise to the surface of the water, with the spawning procedure taking place without any nest building. No plants or any other form of protective material are placed on the

surface but the fish do not seem inclined to consume their own eggs. In any event the fish are removed from the tanks once spawning is over. If there is a large number of eggs — and large specimens can lay more than 10,000 — these are scooped off and placed into larger "cement tanks" with about 20 cm of water in them. The little fish are given water fleas as their initial food and in the first three days crushed, hard boiled egg yolk which, under aquarium conditions can fortunately be replaced by the growth-enhancing but much more controllable, fine-flaked food Tetra MikroMin. In these cement containers the young fish quickly grow to bonny specimens up to 4 to 5 cm which can either be exported as aquarium fish or go on to the next rearing stage as food fish.

If you want to keep these fish in your aquarium, the arrangements for their

general care

should be at least equivalent to those as outlined for the larger aquarium. For growing fish, tanks over 100 cm long will do and those in excess of 160 cm are appropriate for larger specimens. Either way they should be well stocked with plants and robust, so-called hard plants should be given preference over tender subjects.

As the kissing gourami takes its food mainly from the surface, feeding with flaked food such as TetraPhyll — a plant-based substance with a very high proportion of high grade vegetable and vitamin-rich raw materials — and especially Tetra Marin, a large-flaked food with a "seafood" bias with balanced additions of vitamins, is vital if they are to do well. Only well-fed individuals will thrive and grow to their full potential. The "grazing" of algae-covered surfaces that these fish indulge in between feeds is a significant indicator of their high requirement for plant-based food. Any live food in the water or on the tank bed is seldom taken and unless additional food is floated on the surface, a standstill in growth will ensue.

The water temperature should be around 25 °C and a good filtration system will promote the wellbeing of the fish.

The
breeding
of these fish presents rather more problems than is the case with other species of labyrinth fish. Two important factors are prerequisite for breeding success. On the one hand, your breeding stock must be at least 12 to 14 cm long and, on the other, you must have the use of a container that is at least 1 m or, better still, 2 m long and at least 60 cm deep. The water surface should be covered by floating plants, i.e. floating stems of *Rotala rotundifolia*, *Limnophila aquatica* or *Hygrophila difformis*. In some parts dried grass with strong stalks was placed on the surface in order to protect the rising eggs from the attentions of their greedy parents. This produces an important side effect because this dried grass or hay contains eggs that will develop into infusoria that will serve as food for the tiny youngsters.

For rearing these fish the water values play a rather subordinate part. The male produces a seemingly random number of air bubbles that rise to the surface but does not build a bubble nest as such. The pair mate in open water and release the eggs in a some-

what aimless fashion. As this species is very productive, larger specimens are capable of producing up to 10,000 eggs per spawning session. The parent fish should be removed from the tank after spawning. The eggs float to the surface or attach themselves to various plant parts. After about four days at a water temperature of 30 °C the young fish are free swimming and have an almost insatiable appetite right from the start. They need very fine food, a proven variety being Tetra MikroMin, a pulverised flaked food that should be strewn on the surface several times a day. If plenty of good, nutritious food is made available to them, the little *Helostoma temminckii* grow quickly until they have to face another critical period at about four weeks old. It is at this point that the labyrinth mechanism takes over its respiratory function and as the fish now need to come to the surface to take atmospheric air, this should have any "chill" taken off it. The temperature of both water and air should be 30 °C which implies that the container should be well covered.

A typical riverside scene from near Kotawaringin in south west Kalimantan.

It was as recently as 1990 that this familiar species was renamed as *Macropodus ocellatus*. However, until the situation is fully and satisfactorily clarified, we shall continue to refer to it as

◆ *Macropodus chinensis*
(BLOCH, 1790)
the round-tailed paradise fish.

Males of this species attain a total length of up to 8 cm with the females remaining somewhat smaller. For most of the time these fish could well be called "plain as a (grey) church mouse". It is only in his wedding suit that the male becomes a radiant, impressive chap with a marvellous pattern of markings in the most brilliant of colours. The female also changes her colouring at mating time and turns a very light, almost cream colour. The difference between the sexes is very marked. As half-grown specimens the males already have longer dorsal and anal fins whilst females are fuller in the belly parts when spawning time approaches. The sexes can also be differentiated by means of the "x-ray" method, as described under *Trichopsis pumilus*. *Macropodis chinensis* is at home in the south of China where summer temperatures can rise to 30 °C but in winter the mercury may fall to

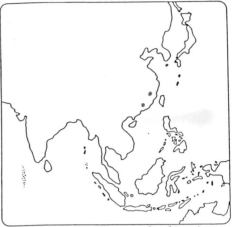

Asiatic distribution of *Macropodus chinensis*.

just about zero. This makes it an ideal subject for keeping in an unheated window sill aquarium or even for the garden pond in areas with a mild climate. They should be kept in well planted aquaria containing a liberal quantity of floating plants. Here the temperature may fluctuate between 10 and 25 °C depending on the season but the warm period should not last for too long as extended exposure to such conditions makes the fish delicate and susceptible to disease.

Macropodus chinensis (Macropodus ocellatus).

The recommendations made for paradise fish (see page 93) also apply to the species first described by Dr. Ernst AHL in 1936, namely

▶ *Macropodus concolor*
(AHL, 1936)

the black paradise fish.

This fish which was characterised in the first description as having a checkered or reticulated pattern is a little larger than the previous species with a total length of about 11 cm.

Generally speaking, the body colour of these creatures is grey but at higher water temperatures or in a threat posture or when displaying, this changes almost to black. The

Macropodus concolor.

fins then become white-edged, with the males exhibiting deep red ventral fins. Here too the females have shorter fins and remain somewhat smaller. From time to time the matter of whether this is an independent species or not comes under discussion. This continues to be the case and no definitive conclusions have yet been reached.

For their

general care

the aquarium should be set up in accordance with the recommendations under *Macropodus opercularis*. As this species is not aggressive, it can be kept in a community tank with practically any other placid type of fish. The water temperature should be a little higher at around 24 to 25 °C.

In terms of

breeding

behaviour, this species conducts itself in the same way as the one described next. The conditions required for raising the young are also similar, though the temperature should be raised to 30 °C. Furthermore, it is advisable to remove the parents from the breeding tank once the fry have reached the free swimming stage. This fish is not as productive as the paradise fish and the young are more delicate. For this reason it is advisable to provide soft, slightly acidic water if they are to develop well.

The paradise fish could almost be regarded as a pioneer of present day fishkeeping. It was back in 1869 that it made the long, difficult trek from China to Europe as the first tropical ornamental fish. Its magnificent colouring and original behaviour were a sensation at the time. A pair of paradise fish fetched the fabulous price of fifty gold marks — in those days the equivalent of a month's income.

The first breeding successes came relatively quickly with this fish that was virtually "worth its weight in gold". Unfortunately, the initial careful selection process with only perfectly coloured stock soon started to relent under financial pressures. Subsequent non selective breeding caused the quality of the available stock to deteriorate drastically. Even today some of the "old hands" still talk about examples that are in a completely different class to our present day specimens.

Asiatic distribution of *Macropodus concolor*.

Courtship display of the black paradise fish.

▶ *Macropodus opercularis*
(LINNAEUS, 1758)

still referred to today as the paradise fish par excellence or simply as the "macropod", ranks as one of the most beautiful and most popular of all aquarium fish. They are capable of reaching a total length of 10 cm but generally stay a little under that mark. Adult males exhibit very fine, long fins with light-bordered extensions to the rays. The females are a little smaller and have shorter fins.

The
natural habitat
is usually defined as south China, Kora, Viet Nam and Formosa. Here the species lives in the paddy fields, water ditches and small streams and in some instances their range stretches into the brackish water zones near the coasts. The fact that their range extends

so far north indicates that they are quite robust creatures. They tolerate temperatures between 10 and 35 °C and have been known to survive in even colder conditions.

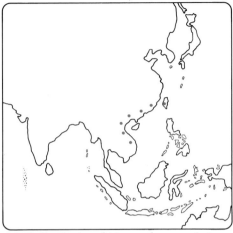

Asiatic distribution of *Macropodus opercularis*.

Macropodus opercularis.

The
general care
of these fish does not present any problems. Dense clumps of plants should be provided in places as hideouts for the females. *Heteranthera zosterifolia, Hygrophila stricta, Bacopa caroliniana* or *Limnophila aquatica,* planted as groups of five to ten will form nice features that will grow up to the water surface. Pieces of bogwood with the occasional *Microsorium pteropus* make a nice contrast to these. The best material for the bed is gravel with a grain size of 1 to 3 mm. The water quality values are secondary. The temperature can lie between 22 and 25 °C which means that normal room temperatures are often adequate. A number of floating plants such as *Ceratopteris pteridoides* and *Riccia flutans* will also fit in well. The aquarium should be well lit, at 0.5 Watts per liter so that the plants can grow well. A good internal filter such as the Brillant Filter with filter chamber will ensure good water circulation and thus clear, clean water.

You should avoid keeping them together with small, peaceable fish because the "macropod" has something of a reputation as an aggressive sort but this applies mainly to its behaviour towards fellows of its own species.

Nor is its
breeding
difficult. Although these fish will reproduce in small containers, a tank with a minimum size of 70 × 30 × 30 cm is recommended as they are a fecund species.

The breeding tank should be set up in the same way as for the normal aquarium. *Macropodus opercularis* is a bubble nest spawner that builds its nest amongst floating plants at the surface of the water. A single pair should be isolated for breeding. Spawning takes place during the typical courtship embrace under the bubble nest, with both parties participating in gathering the eggs and taking them to the nest. On conclusion of these duties the female is driven off by the male who then proceeds to take care of the brood. It is quite plausible that several consecutive broods can grow together in one aquarium because the parents do not molest their offspring, provided they are given enough decent food. Suitable temperatures for breeding are around the 28 °C mark. The youngsters start swimming after about 4 days. As they have such a huge appetite, the recommended first food for these little fellows must be Tetra MikroMin because its high-grade formula of protein, carotin, fats and many other vitamins fulfills the requirements of the young brood to the letter. Tetra MikroMin should be given in small doses several times a day. Later, when the fish are about 1 cm long Tetra Ovin can be relied on to take over the job of providing the appropriate diet specifically for growth. In the breeding tank the Brillant Super Filter is replaced by a Billi-Filter shortly before spawning. This ensures that the powerful effect of the Brillant Filter's wake which could be dangerous to young fish is replaced by the gentler, harmless yet equally effective filtering capacity of the Billi Filter.

Where there is a large shoal of fry, the filter cartridge should be cleaned every two to three days, kneading and squeezing it under flowing tap water to maintain its filtration performance. A partial water change, say a quarter to a third of the contents every eight to ten days, is recommended. The notes on their care and feeding are also important for the other species of labyrinth fish.

Chinese fish farmers use large ceramic vases for breeding *Macropodus opercularis.*

The following rather uncommon species was first described in 1937 by the Singhalese ichthyologist DERANIYAGALA and is known as

◆ *Malpulutta kretseri*
(DERANIYAGALA, 1937)

This is a very dainty little species with the females only reaching 4 cm and the males 6 cm in total length. The 2 cm long extension to the central rays on the caudal fin of the males of the species is not included in this measurement.

As the

natural habitat

the original describer gives Dandegamuva, Kikavaratiya and Hettipola in the north west of the island of Ceylon (Sri Lanka) and Gilimalay in the province of Sabaragamuva. A further location identified for this species is in the south west of the island, about 15 miles north east of the town of Galle. The latter is a rain forest area surrounded by rice fields where the watercourses constitute the tributaries of the great Ging-Gang River in the broadest sense of the term. This district, which has been designated as the Kottawa Forest Reserve, is a small rain forest area where narrow watercourses, still just 2 m wide and up to 40 cm deep, make their way

Asiatic distribution of *Malpulutta kretseri*.

through the jungle, usually completely overgrown by the greenery. The sun's rays scarcely strike the surface of the water so that the picture is one of constant semi darkness. The bed of the streams is made up of sand with a grain size of up to 2 mm and coloured a yellowish brown. Many dead, decaying leaves of the emergent flora cover the bed, offering good hiding places. The bank zones are for the most part overhanging and represent a favourite resting place for these fish. *Malpulutta kretseri* are still

Malpulutta kretseri.

Table No. 4

Locality:	Kottawa Forest 15 miles north east of Galle Sri Lanka
Clarity:	very clear
Colour:	light brownish
pH value:	6.6
D general hardness	4 °dH
D carbonate hardness	2 °dH
Conductivity:	35 microsiemens at 27.5 °C
Nitrite:	0.01 mg/l
Water depth:	up to 40 cm
Water movement:	slight current
Water temperature:	27.5 °C
Date of tests:	28.3.1975
Time:	13.00

regarded as something of a rarity in the amateur aquarium these days. Even in their home waters they are rather uncommon and only small numbers of them are caught.

They are very variable in their

colouring.

Normally their appearance gives the dominant impression of being a greyish brown. When they are slightly agitated though, this changes to a dark, marbled pattern and when very excited this pattern becomes very dark. The fins turn a shade of bluish black. In the males the dorsal, caudal and anal fins are bordered in white.

Unfortunately,

breeding

this species is not all that simple. Aquaria with a length of some 50 cm are quite adequate for the purpose. They are bubble nesters and like to site the nest in cavities or under stones or broad leaves, just a few centimeters from the bed. It is usually a relatively small affair. After a harmonious courtship they spawn underneath the nest, with the male wrapping himself round the female and turning her over with her genital zone uppermost. After a fervent embrace of

about five seconds, during which the eggs emerge and are fertilized, the male lets go of his partner and both sink to the bottom in a form of stupor. After about 30 to 35 seconds the female reawakens and gathers up the eggs, bringing them back to the nest in her mouth. The male wakes up some ten seconds later and immediately starts defending his territory. If there are no other fish present the male too will devote himself to searching and caring for the eggs. However, one can state quite unambiguously that in this species the female is very active in gathering the eggs.

The whole spawning procedure is concluded after about five hours and the male then takes over the sole responsibility for caring for the brood. The embryos need 55 to 60 hours at a water temperature of 27 °C to hatch out of the egg case.

As the tolerances are unfortunately not very great, it is necessary to simulate the natural water values as closely as possible if the young are to make good progress in their development. Only about 15 to 25 fish are swimming after about five days which is a pretty poor crop in numerical terms. Perhaps this is why they are so rare in the wild.

Malpulutta kretseri must be rated as one of the more "tender" or "delicate" of the labyrinth fish.

The aquarium recommended for

general care

of this species is the smaller version of the two. A plentiful stock of good plants, with cavities formed from rocks and coconut shells should figure in the decoration. Clean, well filtered water with a low nitrite content is an important prerequisite for healthy conditions. The tanks must be well covered as these fish are good jumpers.

As far as

feeding

is concerned, sun- or freeze-dried aquatic invertebrates such as the red mosquito larvae in TetraDelica, alternating with a flaked food such as TetraMin as a vitamin-rich dietary supplement should be used together with TetraPhyll as a vegetable supplement.

A species that is also encountered on the island of Sri Lanka though it is not endemic there, being found in the ornamental ponds of the major hotels and state-run guest houses as well as being raised as a food fish, is

◆ *Osphronemus goramy*
(LACEPEDE, 1802)   28-30"
the giant gourami.

This fish, farmed nowadays as a commercial species in many parts of Asia, is the biggest representative of the labyrinth fish family. It grows up to 70 cm long and as such is only suitable for keeping in very large tanks. Its somewhat plump appearance, the rounded head shape and the large protruding mouth, make it look like a pleasant, comical chap. In its juvenile form, that is up to about 15 cm long, its appearance is very

different; then the pointed head, the dark grey body colour with dark transverse stripes, would not make you suspect that this was *Osphronemus goramy* at all. It is only as it continues to grow that the head shape and colour start to change.

The acutal
natural habitat
is very hard to tie down nowadays because of its wide distribution as a commercially farmed fish, since it turns up in this role in widespread areas of tropical and subtropical Asia. The giant gourami is mostly raised for the table in artificial open air ponds. It has a very delicate taste. Fully grown specimens reach a length of 70 cm and weigh up to 7 kg. As they are good "keepers" under normal conditions and at high temperatures, they are an interesting commercial proposi-

Osphronemus goramy, young specimen about 15 cm long.

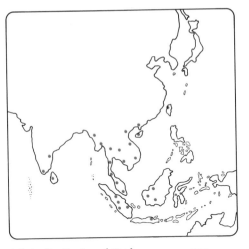

Asiatic distribution of *Osphronemus goramy*.

The nest itself is sited in the dense plant growth of the bank zones. It has a diameter of around 50 cm and is some 25 cm high, with the highest part lying just below the water surface and the hemispherical section reaching downwards where it finally forms a flat part. The core of this knot of vegetation is filled with soft, decaying leaves. The pair then spawns under this screen of matter after the courtship embrace. Adult gouramis are very productive. Fish breeders have told me that 20,000 eggs are no rare occurrence and the count is often higher. Once spawning is over, the male takes care of the nest. If they want to ensure the best results in terms of productivity, it is best to transfer the core of the nest with the spawn to large cement tanks so that progress can be properly monitored. When the fish have reached a length of 3 to 4 cm, i.e. at the age of three to four weeks, the fish are again transferred to specially prepared open air tanks. As giant gouramis are very greedy and eat any leftovers of rice, salad and fruit they may be given, as well as the standard fare of pig manure, they soon grow into fine examples of a saleable size.

tion. They are kept in the aforementioned open air aquatic "fields" about 10 × 20 m in size and about 1 m deep where they will grow within 30 to 36 months into point of sale specimens. They are fed almost exclusively on pig manure. In fact you often see pig sties built on stilts directly over the fish ponds. Their floors consist of wooden slats on which the pigs live but designed to allow the manure to fall straight into the water. This has a twofold benefit. First, all that is needed to clean the sty is simply to hose down the slats with water and secondly, that the fish have a direct supply of vitamin-rich food. This arrangement is often used for the rearing of other species of commercially farmed fish. With this kind of regime young giant gouramis will reach a length of 25 cm after just one year. It is only possible to breed from them once a year. Two year old giant gouramis are ready to commence reproduction only at the start of the rainy season, probably induced by the presence of so much fresh water and the associated cooling of their biotope. For this process the males build a hemispherical nest made from plant parts. A few bubbles are put in the middle but only in the flat lower part. The males are adept at tearing off bits of plants growing just above the water surface for their nest building.

Two year old sub adult specimen about 40 cm long.

A species of labyrinth fish that has recently been imported live by A. WERNER and subsequently studied by Dr. W. FOERSCH is

▶ *Parasphaerichthys ocellatus*
(PARASHAD and MUKERJI, 1929)

This is a kind of fish that is very similar to *Sphaerichthys osphromenoides* types but which only attains total lengths of around 4 cm and as such is a good bit smaller. Moreover, they have a more "streched" body shape and a more pointed head. Their tail fin is rounded. Seen from above, they have a broader body and look altogether heftier. The ocelli — eye-like markings that figure in their specific name — are not all that often seen and even then remain just faint flecks on their sides. FOERSCH kept the two specimens of *Parasphaerichthys ocellatus* that have as yet been imported in a small, well planted aquarium filled with soft water. The fish lived a retiring lifestyle and were very shy. On the basis of his observations, we can assume that low water temperatures around 20 to 22 °C suit it best.

Asiatic distribution of *Parasphaerichthys ocellatus*.

Its

natural habitat
is to be found in the higher mountains of northern Burma. The locations in which they were found were, according to the notes of the ichthyologists who described them, some cloudy steams running alongside the Kamaing Jade Mines Road, a few miles out of Kamaing.

Parasphaerichthys ocellatus.

Barbara BROWN took the very unusual step of naming a new dwarf labyrinth fish in honour of her husband Allan. This fish is

▶ *Parosphromenus allani*
(BROWN, 1987)

This description was accepted, though it does not conform with current practice. As well as *P. allani*, a second species was also put forward with the name of *Parosphromenus harveyi*. Both "species" show similarities to *P. deissneri*. These fish all exhibit remarkable parallels in terms of their general care requirements and reproductive behaviour. *P. allani* is a native of Sarawak (North Borneo) and is a typical fish of the acidic to very adidic waters with a low mineral content that prevail there. Given the appropriate water conditions, they are not problematical subjects for the aquarium. Water quality is the prime factor. There have already been a number of successful attempts at breeding these little bubble nesters. The species has a preference for spawning in little

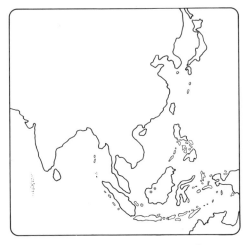

Asiatic distribution of *Parosphromenus allani*.

cavities. Once they have hatched, the fry can remain in the breeding tank with their parents and with the right kind of feeding on newly hatched Artemia salina will rapidly grow to full size.

Parosphromenus allani.

Another species of this genus that we were able to bring back alive from the Kapuas region in 1990 will be referred to here as

▶ *Parosphromenus anjunganensis*
(KOTTELAT, 1991)

These fish that grow to around 3.5 cm long are occasionally to be found living in the same biotope as the species *Parosphromenus ornaticauda*. It seems that they have something of a preference for less acidic water though. In the habitat that we were able to find, the deep-brown coloured, clear, slightly flowing water was also very soft and, with a pH value 5.4, very acidic. The conductivity was only 22 microsiemens at a water temperature of 28.3 °C. We came across the fish in a small river around 7 km south west of Anjungan, on the road from Pontianak to Sanggau in West Kalimantan (Kalimantan-Barat). They are said to occur also in the Mandor River 20 km to the east

Parosphromenus anjunganensis.

which gives it a somewhat wider range. This dwarf labyrinth fish is also one of the bubble nesters that prefers sheltered crannies amongst aquatic plants as its favoured spawning and general living quarters.

Parosphromenus anjunganensis.

Another species that belongs amongst the dwarves of the labyrinth fish kingdom is

◗ *Parosphromenus deissneri*
(BLEEKER, 1859)

also known as DEISSNER's dwarf macropod.

This reaches a total length of just 4 cm. In their courtship colouring it is easy to tell the two sexes apart. Besides having two dark longitudinal stripes, the males show lots of red and brown tones in their fins and the entire outer edge of these has a turquoise trim. The females on the other hand retain their yellowish brown day to day attire.

Parosphromenus deissneri.

Asiatic distribution of *Parosphromenus deissneri*.

The
natural habitat
was for a long time thought to be confined to the island of Bangka near Sumatra. Nowadays we know that its range extends to the island of Sumatra itself and even to the Malaysian peninsula. The fish live in narrow, gently flowing watercourses. Their favourite haunts appear to be the shallow margins of the bank zones or flooded, shady, densely overgrown shallow stretches of water. Here the water itself is very clean with a dark brown colour, altogether a very similar habitat to that of *Sphaerichthys o. osphromenoides,* the chocolate gourami.

The
general care
of these dwarf macropods does present problems. You need to set up a smaller type of tank with plenty of growing plants and items of decoration designed to provide small cavities in and amongst rocks, pieces of bogwood and coconut shells.

The water values must be as low as possible. General and carbonate hardness figures around 3° dH are needed and the acidity of the water should be around the pH5 mark.

Very good filtration over filter peat and water conditioning over active peat are essential. In order to maintain a certain degree of water stability, an aquarium size of 70 cm long by 40 cm wide and 30 cm deep is advisable. The water temperature should be set at 25 °C. As these fish are rather timid, only other small species with an equally placid temperament should be kept with them. The aquarium should be sited in a quiet corner and lit in the normal fashion.

For
breeding
purposes a pair of this species should be put into a small aquarium about 50 cm long which should be set up in the same way as for normal care. Here too, important features are one or two rocky cavities incorporating a roof under which the male can shelter his bubble nest and eggs. Another possibility would be an upturned flower pot placed slightly on its side or with an access hole knocked out. The water temperature can be raised to 26 °C and the water values lowered still further so that the pH value is around 4.8. The onset of mating is announced by the fact that the male will now tolerate the presence of the female in and around the cavity that holds his little bubble nest. As the pair embrace, the eggs emerge and are conveyed by the male to his cavity where he spits them out so that they stick to the roof. The larvae hatch after about 65 hours and the young fish start to swim around freely after about seven days. As their first food they take the newly hatched nauplii of *Artemia salina*.

A regular water change involving a quarter of the tank contents every week, using water that has been prepared beforehand to suit the given requirements, will promote growth and healthy development of these infant dwarves. Until just a few years ago nothing was known about the successful care and breeding of this species. It is thanks to the research efforts of Dr. Walter FOERSCH of Munich that we now know so much about the behaviour and breeding biology of *P. deissneri*.

Yet another very small labyrinth fish is

◗ Parosphromenus filamentosus
(VIERKE, 1981)

This new species shows similarities to *P. deissneri*. However, males of *P. filamentosus* do not have a round shape to the dorsal fin but more of a lance-shaped outline which is drawn out into a thread-like extension. The females, which give the overall impression of being altogether more rounded in the belly area, have the same colouring as the males, albeit rather less intense. Their fins are generally somewhat shorter. They also have a lengthening of the rays in the caudal fin though this is less pronounced.

The

natural habitat
of this species is found around the town of Banjarmasin in Kalimantan in the south of the island of Borneo. The waters where it occurs are usually gently flowing, brownish, soft streams with water temperatures around 27 °C and a pH value of about 5 to 5.5.

For the

general care
of these fish you should provide separate, smallish, shallow tanks decorated with lots of aquatic plants and structures offering nooks and crannies as hideouts. This is a more robust species than *P. deissneri* and therefore an easier subject to keep. Even so,

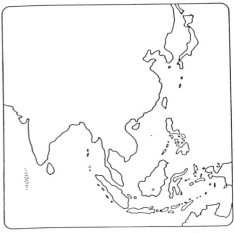

Asiatic distribution of *Parosphromenus filamentosus.*

a regular water change every 8–10 days is recommended. This fish should be fed exclusively on live food.

Breeding
may take place in this species in the usual everyday tank. But if your specific intention is to raise quantities of them it is advisable to keep them in isolated pairs in a separate breeding tank. These fish usually spawn in cavities under a little bubble nest with the male undertaking the brood care duties. The youngsters are swimming around after about 6 days at water temperatures around 27 °C and at this point need very small food.

Parosphromenus filamentosus.

The second species of dwarf labyrinth fish that was described in a very unusual fashion by B. BROWN as

▶ *Parosphromenus harveyi*
(BROWN, 1987)

first came to our attention in an English aquarium magazine article in which no details about the morphology of the species are given. For this reason Jürgen SCHMIDT commented as follows in "IGL-Macropoden", edition of 4/89, on the appearance of this fish: "I can only differentiate Harvey's dwarf gourami, *Parosphromenus harveyi*, from *P. deissneri* by the absence of any red-orange in the display colouring of the fins and by a less drab appearance of the normal female coloration. This species apparently reaches a length of 3.5 cm. The fish from the type locality exhibit, like all the species in this group. two longitudinal stripes on a light ground in their normal colouring. Black flecks are seldom found on the dorsal fin. Females are coloured yellow in

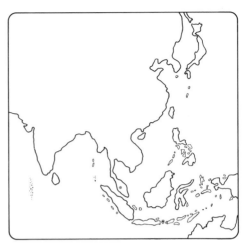

Asiatic distribution of *Parosphromenus harveyi*.

the back region and a reddy brown edge is to be seen on the dorsal fin." The species has been demonstrated as occurring in Battu Arang, province of Selangor in West Malaysia. It has bred successfully on occasions but it must be regarded as a very rare species.

Parosphromenus harveyi.

On their collecting trip through Kalimantan in 1990 Norbert NEUGEBAUER and the author discovered another of these dwarf species of labyrinth fish which was described as

◆ *Parosphromenus spec.*
(KOTTELAT, 1991)

As far as we can tell, this new species attains a total length of around 3.5 cm. From the standpoint of their external appearance these fish bear a resemblance to *Parosphromenus filamentosus* by virtue of the pronounced lengthening of the middle ray of the caudal fin. But what appears to be the typical distinguishing feature of this new fish is the small double spot on the side of the body. In their display dress the fish take on a wine red colouring and the males exhibit a conspicuous white edging to their fins. The species lives in a swampy area 2 km north of Sukamara and also 4 km south west of Pudukuali in the south western part of Central Kalimantan (Kalimantan-Tengah).

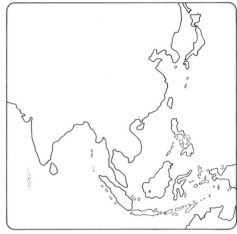

Asiatic distribution of *Parosphromenus linkei* from Pudukuali.

In the same biotope we encountered, together with many other species of fish, yet another new dwarf of the same group which we called *Parosphromenus spec.* from Sukamara.

Parosphromenus linkei.

There are parallels to *P. deissneri* in the west Malaysian species

Parosphromenus nagyi
(SCHALLER, 1985)

though any comparison will show that it differs from that species by the absence of stripes in its display dress and a completely different body colour and ventral fin colouring. An interesting feature is the complete absence of any red. It is fully grown at 5.5 cm long. It requires similar living conditions to *P. deissneri*, the only difference being that several individuals, if possible in largish groups, should be kept in a good sized aquarium. Water quality is a very important factor and the water values of its homeland should be borne strictly in mind if they are to do well in the aquarium. *P. nagyi* comes from the eastern side of the Malaysian peninsula in the vicinity of Kuantan where it lives in association with *Sphaerichthys o. osphromenoides*, *Betta tussyae* and occasionally with *Betta imbellis*, amongst others.

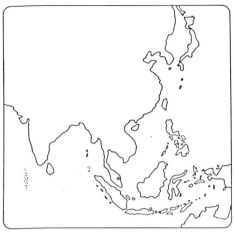

Asiatic distribution of *Parosphromenus nagyi*.

Albert WASER (1985) has recorded the following details on the biotope: "The water is the colour of dark tea with a pH value of 4.3 and a conductivity figure measured at 50 microsiemens. At midday the water had a temperature of 26 °C. At the time of our expedition there was a severe drought on the

Parosphromenus nagyi.

east coast which meant that the water level was low."

My own investigations took place in January which is to say at high water level after the main rainy season in the months of November and December. Starting out from the sea, we went in a westerly direction through Kuantan, around 2 km before Gambang, highway 19 begins leading south towards Segamat. I drove down this road for another 5 kilometers to around 150 meters beyond the 147 km marker to Segamat (or conversely 33 km to Kuantan) and commenced my investigations at this point. In this very dry, partly cultivated bush land-scape, which has some gentle hills here and there, there is a smallish watercourse that passes under the carriageway under a concrete bridge, scarcely visible from the road itself. The bridge has two tunnelled conduits, suitably sized to allow the passage of any amount of water even during the most torrential downpours. This water-course lies in a most picturesque setting, about 6 meters below road level, and flows in narrow channels through an area of grassy marshland. The catch records from here were absolutely nil, as the fish have an ideal escape route under the roots of the floating carpet of plants. However, we did manage to catch a few things in the quiet margins, especially near to the bridge, notably some *Betta pugnax (?)*, *Betta waseri*, some barbs, a spiney eel and three *Parosphromenus nagyi* — two males and a female, including a fine pair, with the male in particularly fine fettle. He was a very well fed specimen. These fish were found in the shallower parts of the water where the throughflow of water was lower and where there was plentiful foliage and abundant emergent plant growth. The pH value here was 4.9 (by fluid means) or 4.63 (by electronic means) with a conduc-tivity of 9 microsiemens at 24.1 °C. The measurements were carried out at around noon in conditions that were at times very overcast but with some sunny intervals.

The period of high water offers an ideal habitat for all fish here. As the water falls again with the advance of the drought

period which usually comes to a head in July or August, all that often remains are small rivulets, often just a few centimeters deep. In places there are also some small, deeper pond-like expanses. The carpets of plants that are borne aloft by their buoyancy during the rainy season then sink and rest on the ground. There are some deeper parts containing water that remain protected from the fierce heat by the plant cover. This provides a new, almost typical habitat for some species, to help them through the drought. It offers protection against enemies above and below the water and the dense matted carpet of plants acts as a protective temperature regulator over these stretches of residual water, preventing it from over heating or drying out completely. This "survival cell" is of special benefit to *Betta* species and it is not unusual to come across *Betta splendens* in such biotopes. Here in the area around Kuantan where very acidic waters predominate in places, one finds that it is *Betta tussyae* that takes advantage of these small patches of water, as reported by WASER and KRUMACHER (1985) based on their experience there in the months of June and July.

They occur, in fact, in surroundings where one would have good grounds for doubting the existence of any fish at all, given that there is often only a centimeter or two of water in places and that often over grown with grass and plants. What does undoubtedly help survival in these so-called drought periods is the fact that there are the occasional heavy falls of rain. All the same by the time the drought does come to an end, it would be more appropriate to talk in terms of these fish living in a concentrate of residual water, though the values will scarcely have altered. Many authors refer to this as a "thickening" of the water. It is only with the onset of the monsoon rains in November that the water is "diluted" once more and the washing down of the dead plant debris such as leaves etc. lying around on the ground helps to acidify the fresh, soft rain water on its way into the streams and rivers. This it does to a marked extent, col ouring the water at the same time. The slight hange in the water values that takes place lso seems to be the trigger for many species o commence their reproductive cycle. In ddition, the rising water level which causes artial flooding of many areas, induces the evelopment of tiny invertebrate life in this often very acidic watery milieu and these insects and larvae are a vital food source for the young fish. Around 2—3 months later, as my investigations in January showed, you can see very many half-grown youngsters living in the dense vegetation.

iotope of *Parosphromenus nagyi* about 33 km south west of Kuantan on highway 19 to Segamat.

One of the smallest and most beautiful of these Parosphromenus species was first imported by Dr. M. KOTTELAT in June 1990 and described as

▶ *Parosphromenus ornaticauda*
(KOTTELAT, 1991)

apparently attains total lengths of only 2.5 cm when fully grown and as such is the smallest of all the representatives of this genus. Their colouring can only be described as truly magnificent. Two months later we managed to import some further specimens and since then we have had the first of their offspring swimming around in our aquarium. They are bubble nest builders that require small cavities on hand if they are to breed. The young fish have no problem in taking newly hatched *Artemia salina* as their first food.

The species comes from the Kapuas area in the region between Sungei Penjuh and Anjungan, north west of Pontianak in West Kalimantan (Kalimantan Barat). Our catching ground was 8 km south west of Anjungan, on the road from Pontianak to Sanggau. The habitat in question was a blackwater stream with very soft, very acidic (pH 4.5), almost standing water. The electrical con-

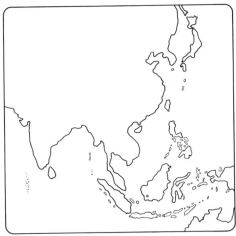

Asiatic distribution of *Parosphromenus ornaticauda.*

ductivity was 39 microsiemens at a water temperature of 27.6 °C. The fish were caught amongst the dense tangle of plants growing on the banks. This species lives here in the company of others, including *Betta spec.* from Mandor, *Betta spec.* from Anjungan and, particularly worthy of note, a second species of *Parosphromenus* that we were able to uncover in conjunction with it just one kilometer away to the east.

Parosphromenus ornaticauda.

Another rather tiny species from this genus is

▶ *Parosphromenus paludicola*
(TWEEDIE, 1952)

Records to date indicate that this fish attains a total length of only 3 cm. Nothing is yet known about sexual differentiation. For a long time nobody had succeeded in importing the species live and it was only in 1979 that I managed to catch some 15 of them and bring them back to Germany for the first time.

Its

natural habitat

is to be found in West Malaysia on the main peninsula. Individuals had hitherto been found on the northern part of the east coast, in the area of Trengganu within the catchment area of the Trengganu River, near to the town of Kuala Brang and Kampong Marchang in small, flowing watercourses of the swampy forests. Usually these are small watercourses that flow in places through cultivated plantations and in doing so pass through dense plant growth comprising trees and a high canopy of branches and leaves that cuts out almost all the sunlight. The specimens shown here were caught in a stream near the town of Kuala Brang with gently flowing water and a temperature of 26 °C. The general and carbonate hardness

Asiatic distribution of *Parosphromenus paludicola*.

Parosphromenus paludicola.

111

levels were both under 1° dH. The conductivity was 6 microsiemens, measured at a water temperature of 26°C. The pH value was 5.5. The water was very clear and a light brownish colour. Heavy sedimentation of iron in flaked form was lying on the plants and on the banks. The water was 50 cm deep. *Parosphromenus paludicola* could mostly be found in the overgrown bank zones, sometimes in water only 5 cm deep. The stream had an average width of two meters.

For their
general care
we have come to the following conclusions. As this species, together with the other two, must be ranked amongst the smaller and more delicate types, they should only be kept in small tanks that allow constant and precise monitoring of their condition and behaviour. They likewise require soft, acidic water values and a low mineral content. As these fish are an absolute delight to behold, you should do without any tank bed material so as to give a better view of them and to provide "clean" conditions for their care. Small cavities should also be included in the decoration, as recommended for the species *Parosphromenus deissneri,* together with a few plants such as *Microsorium pteropus.* A partial water change every five to seven days is advisable, using water prepared in advance by filtration over peat. Although these creatures give the impression of being tough, these recommendations should be observed.

The
breeding
of this species has parallels to *P. deissneri.* The fry grow very slowly.

A small watercourse at the edge of the jungle near Kuala Brang, the habitat of *Parosphromenus paludicola* in West Malaysia.

Another species that is scarcely known to most aquarists and has been seen by few people is

▶ *Parosphromenus parvulus*
(VIERKE, 1979)

Those specimens, that have been found reached total lengths of slightly more than 30 mm.

They differ from the species already dealt with by virtue of the lower number of hard rays in their anal fin and a narrower dorsal fin. They are also differently coloured and their pattern of markings sets them apart from the others too.

The
natural habitat
was stated in the original description as being the Mentaya River system, 250 km north west of Banjarmasin in South Borneo. Four specimens of this species were caught there by Mrs. E. KORTHAUS and Dr. W. FOERSCH, who wrote: "We found this new labyrinth fish in a small, slow flowing stream, the water of which was cola coloured but at the same time clear and transparent."

The water temperature was given as 24 °C, measured at 8.00 in the morning. The pH value was under 4.8. The water had an electrical conductivity of 75 microsiemens, measured at a water temperature of 24 °C.

Asiatic distribution of *Parosphromenus parvulus*.

The fish kept to a dense clump of plants and could only be caught with some difficulty.

For their
general care
you should provide just a small aquarium up to 50 cm long, dotted with plants such as *Microsorium pteropus* and without any covering to the tank bottom so as to enable the whole affair to be kept clean. The water values should be low with the GH and KH not higher than 3° dH and a pH of about 5 to 5.5.

Parosphromenus parvulus.

There is a very small species that I have wrongly regarded as synonymous with *P. parvulus* and which will be referred to here until a complete, definitive identification is carried out, as

▶ *Parosphromenus spec. affin. parvulus*
from Palangkaraya.

In 1988 the author and Jürgen KNEP-PEL were able to verify the existence of this species of labyrinth fish which grows to a mere 2.5 cm in the area north of Palangka-raya, about 180 km north west of Banjar-masin in Central Kalimantan (Kalimantan Tengah). This is around 100 km further east from locations that were proven *P. parvulus* sites, which is a long way for this tiny laby-rinth fish genus. The fish lives in close asso-ciation with many other species of labyrinth fish, including *Sphaerichthys acrostoma* and *Betta edithae*. The deep-brown coloured water was very soft and, with a pH value of 4.1, very acidic too. The electrical conduc-tivity was 24 microsiemens at a water tem-perature of 28.2 °C in the shallow bank zones. *Parosphromenus spec. affin. parvulus*

Asiatic distribution of *Parosphromenus spec. affin. parvulus.*

has been bred by the author but only with modest success. The species is a bubble nest builder that prefers little cavities for this purpose. For their breeding and general care it is very important that the water values reflect those of their natural habitat with water quality being vital too.

Parosphromenus spec. affin parvulus.

114

This other very beautifully coloured *P. dessneri*-type dwarf fish was found in July 1990 in the south west of Kalimantan.

◗ *Parosphromenus spec.*
from Sukamara

In this species the males are especially boldly coloured and grow to a length of about 3 cm. It was interesting to note that they live in a biotope that houses many other species, including a second hitherto unknown type of Parosphromenus, identified as *P. linkei*. These fish all live in an overgrown, extensive area of swampland about 2 km north of Sukamara in the direction of Pudukuali. It is a blackwater biotope with flowing water in parts. A narrow wooden causeway about one and a half kilometers long represents the only means of communication with the land to the north. This gangway over the swamp constitutes a very good observation platform over some interesting waters. The water here is coloured a very dark brown shade. The GH and KH figures were both under 1. The electrical conductivity was measured at 9 microsiemens at a water tem-

Asiatic distribution of *Parosphromenus spec.* from Sukamara.

perature of 24 °C. Measurements were made in the morning after some copious rainfalls. *P. spec.* from Sukamara were very numerous in this area and were found principally in shallow, densely overgrown bank zones or where there was plentiful plant growth.

Parosphromenus spec. from Sukamara.

A species that is found predominantly in the north western areas of the island of Sri Lanka is the little labyrinth fish

▶ *Pseudosphromenus cupanus*
(CUVIER and VALENCIENNES, 1831)

the spike-tailed paradise fish.

These fish are still often referred to these days by their now invalid scientific name of *Macropodus cupanus cupanus*. As adults they reach a total length of 6 cm and can be classed as very placid and even rather shy fish. The characteristics that help sexual differentiation are the usually pointed and elongated shape of the dorsal and caudal fins of the males. Often there is only a slight change of telling the sexes apart at all because these features are only displayed by

Pseudosphromenus cupanus.

116

fully grown specimens. Even then, the females do not always retain the round tail shape but develop a pointed extension to the caudal fin, as in the males. Clearly, differentiation is simple when the fish are wearing their courtship attire. The males then show a great deal more colour against a much lighter body while the females are very dark, almost black.

The
natural habitat
of these fish is found in south east India, the coastal lowlands along the Coromandel coast, some pockets in the western region of the Malabar coast, together with the north western parts of Sri Lanka. Here they live in narrow, gently flowing watercourses, to some extent in the ditches around paddy fields and in accumulations of water and small rivers in the rain forests.

Asiatic distribution of *Pseudosphromenus cupanus*.

The
general care
of the spike-tailed paradise fish is easy because they are very undemanding subjects. All they require is a very small aquarium set up in the style of the "small aquarium for labyrinth fish". In any event, little

cavities or halved coconut shells should be provided near the tank bottom and dense clumps of plants are recommended. The bed should consist of fine gravel with a diameter of up to 3 mm and a few plants of *Ceratopteris pteridoides* floating on the surface will complete the picture. A gentle water movement such as produced by a Brillant Filter is recommended. The water temperature should be around 25 °C and adequate lighting at a rate of 0.5 Watts per liter is important.

Breeding
these fish is not difficult. Aquaria about 50 cm long by 30 cm wide and 30 cm high are adequate. The water level does not need to be more than 20 cm deep. Overhanging pieces of bogwood, with upturned, half-broken flower pots or crevices in the rocks should be provided to assist them in siting their bubble nests. Stands of long-stemmed plants like *Hygrophila corymbosa* are an essential prerequisite for breeding success, as is a water temperature of around 28 °C. The lighting for the breeding aquarium must be quite subdued and the tank should stand in a quiet position. Any unnecessary meddling with the aquarium disturbs the fish and makes them timid. Well established aquaria with a light coating of green algae are preferred by this species for breeding purposes.

The male builds a compact little nest in a cave or under bits of bogwood under which the pair then spawn after wrapping themselves in the usual embrace. A spawning phase lasts about 12 seconds. While the female is still gripped by the spawning stupor, the male breaks away and begins gathering the eggs as they fall to the bottom. Just a few seconds later the female also awakens and takes part in collecting the eggs and bringing them back to the nest. The initial spawning phases only produce about two to four eggs but the number subsequently rises to 12 to 20. The eggs have a diameter of ca 1.2 mm, are oval shaped and have a light yellow colour. Spawning is concluded after around four hours and the male takes over the care of the brood. In doing so he displays very little aggression towards the female. It is true that he will drive her away from the direct vicinity of the nest but he will tolerate her within sight of it. After about 48 hours at a water temperature of 27°C the embryos hatch and hang like little white dots with transparent tails in the nest. The eye pigmentation can be clearly seen. After a further 24 hours this marking becomes more pronounced and one can make out the shape of a tiny fish. The yolk sac has already become very small. After another 24 hours, that is four days after spawning, the young fish are fully developed. The eyes are clearly visible and a

lightly spotted protective pattern can be seen covering the body. The yolk sac has disappeared entirely and a few hours later they are swimming freely.

Unfortunately, *Pseudosphromenus cupanus* does not rank amongst the most colourful of the labyrinth fish. In the aquaria of most dealers they come over as being grey and drab. They only show their full beauty if they are given proper care and attention. It is only then that they will display the sort of attractive appearance and interesting behaviour that make them truly captivating subjects for the amateur fishkeeper.

Different phases of the act of spawning in *Pseudosphromenus cupanus*. They build their compact little bubble nest under bits of bogwood and in caves.

◆ *Pseudosphromenus dayi*
(KOHLER, 1909)

also known as the red spike-tailed paradise fish.

These fish already look very attractive when they are still juveniles. They are fully grown at about 7 cm long, though the females remain rather shorter. The males have pointed, elongated dorsal and anal fins and the extension to middle rays of the caudal fin is particularly pronounced.

Pseudosphromenus dayi.

The
natural habitat

is stated as the coastal lowlands of the Coromandel coastline in south east India and the coast region of west Malaysia. However, there is serious doubt about this latter part of their range because none have been caught there recently.

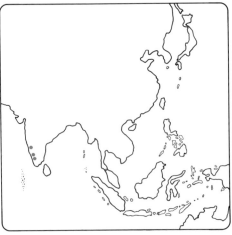

Asiatic distribution of *Pseudosphromenus dayi*.

The
general care

of this species is straightforward. They are peaceable fish and very suitable subjects for keeping in a community tank together with other species, including smaller ones. However, the aquarium should not be too small and minimum dimensions of 70 cm long by 30 cm wide and high are recommended. Various groups of tall-stemmed plants such as *Hygrophila difformis*, synonymous with *Synnema triflorum*, *Hygrophila corymbosa* as well as *Vallisneria spiralis*, the common eel grass and a few examples of floating plants like *Ceratopteris pteridoides* and *Pistia stratiotes*, the water lettuce, should be provided. Nor should there be any lack of cavities and bits of bogwood. The water temperature can be around the 26 °C mark. The aquarium can be lit in the standard way at a rate of 0.5 Watts per liter. The form of aquarium chosen for the red spike-tailed paradise fish can be either that of the "small"

or "large aquarium for labyrinth fish". This fish is happy to eat flaked food of all types.

For
breeding

the aquarium can be set up in the normal way but with the temperature raised slightly to 30 °C. This fish does frequently build its compact little bubble nest in cavities but it often sites it at the water surface under plant leaves. Alternatively, it may opt to place it in a corner without any additional anchor. Mating is usually a harmonious affair. The female is often allowed to take part in the brood care operations.

Pseudosphromenus dayi in a courtship embrace under their bubble nest.

With the genus *Spaerichthys* we come to a group of labyrinth fish that are rather more problematical to keep, broadly known as the chocolate gouramis. It is only recently that additional members of this group, apart from the type species, have become known. One of these is

▶ *Sphaerichthys acrostoma*
(VIERKE, 1979)

This fish grows to over 6 cm in length and as such is larger than the other species in this genus. In comparison with the rest its body colour is much less vivid and indeed, a much feebler shade of brown. The dorsal, caudal and anal fins are all edged with a very delicate shade of light blue. Its essential distinctive characteristics as compared with the other species are the much more pointed head shape and the very stretched body form.

The
natural habitat
of this new species is found in Borneo.

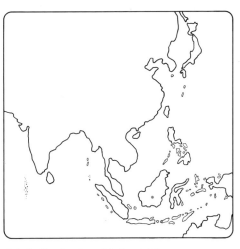

Asiatic distribution of *Sphaerichthys acrostoma*.

Specimens were caught in the Mentaya river system, 250 km north west of Benjarmasin, in the course of a collecting expedition undertaken by Frau E. KORTHAUS and Frau and Dr. FOERSCH.

Sphaerichthys acrostoma.

Since then I have personally been able to make a trip to investigate the natural habitat of this uncommon and practically unknown species. The area in which we set out to catch this fish lay in the region around Palangkaraya in Central Kalimantan. Large areas of the rainforest have been cleared so that the landscape has been turned into a swampy scrubland. Around 27 kilometers north of Palangkaraya the water running out of this marshland flows into a clear, dark brown river bed with quite a noticeable current. Here the pH value was 4.2 and the electrical conductivity was measured at 20 microsiemens at a water temperature of 28 °C. The river bed was partly made up of large stones sitting on fine white sand. It did not seem to contain any marsh or aquatic plants. It was only in some shallow lagoon-like stretches that were almost screened off by sandbanks that we found parts that were overgrown with grass-like plants that provided protection. In this dense plant growth we were able to find, together with quite an array of other species, three very uncommon types of labyrinth fish. One of these was the sub species of chocolate gourami rather numerous here, *Sphaerichthys osphromenoides selatanensis*, and what is possibly a species endemic to here, a little kind of *Parosphromenus spec.*, also abundant in these waters. In contrast, the third species of labyrinth fish, *Sphaerichthys acrostoma*, was rare. We were only able to catch seven specimens, all about 3 cm long, in spite of a great deal of effort. To begin with they presented little in the way of problems in the aquarium. Bearing in mind the water values measured in their natural habitat i.e. soft water with a pH value between 4.5 and 5, their general care was straightforward. However, the decisive thing was and still is water quality, for which the essential requirements are regular water changes and sufficient filtration capacity. Some largish groups of fernlike plants and pieces of bogwood will do for decoration. These will serve as hiding places for the fish which, combined with subdued lighting, help them to overcome their natural timidity. All species of *Sphaerichthys* are easy to keep

under these conditions and will breed readily. In their adult size sexual differentiation in *S. acrostoma* is not difficult. The male can be distinguished from the female quite clearly by the reddish longitudinal stripe behind his eye and the rather more pointed shape to his dorsal fin. Mating is preceded by an impressive courtship display in which the male plays a very active part. The prospective mates start to associate with each other a number of days beforehand. Unlike *S. osphromenoides* and its sub species *S. selatanensis*, in which the females care for the brood in their mouth, in *S. acrostoma* it is the male that undertakes these duties. With his hugely extended throat sack he will spend the period after spawning hidden amongst plants, turning over the brood at regular intervals with the distinctive, typical chewing movements. At a water temperature of 27 °C or so, it is about a fortnight before the male starts to release the 7 mm long fry in little batches throughout the day. There may be around 40 of these little, dark-coloured *S. acrostoma* which immediately start taking newly hatched nauplii of *Artemia salina*, despite the fact that they still have very small mouths. Remarkably, in comparison with young *S. o. selatanensis*, the fry of *S. acrostoma* are very fast growing. In just three weeks they can be 13 to 15 mm long and have already taken on the high-backed shape typical of the species. Their appearance also changes. The front half of the fish turns a light brown colour whilst the rear part of the body becomes very dark, almost black. The caudal fin remains colourless and unmarked. By the age of two months they have reached an average length of 3.5 cm and have an insatiable appetite. These fish are fully grown at about a year old by which time they will have attained a total length of some 7.5 cm, though the females are rather shorter. Both sexes have very pointed fins. In addition, the males exhibit a dark, light-edged longitudinal stripe in the middle of the body. At this point the specimens that we had proceeded to breed as F1 generation individuals. The successful outcome consisted of 35 fry.

When that great pioneer of the aquarium hobby, J. REICHELT of Conradshöhe near Berlin, wrote in 1906 of his vain attempts to bring the chocolate gourami, then still known as the live-bearing *Osphromenus malayanus*, back to Germany from Singapore and Sumatra, little did he realise that he was introducing us to a fish that still presents us with considerable difficulties some eighty years on. Nowadays we know that the fish in question was, in fact,

▶ *Sphaerichthys osphrome-noides osphromenoides*
(CANESTRINI, 1860)

the chocolate gourami.

This species is fully grown at a total length of 5 cm. Sexual differentiation is not difficult. The dorsal and anal fins have a bold light edge to them, as do the upper and lower parts of the caudal fin. In the male the dorsal fin is pointed, while that of the female is gently rounded.

The
natural habitat
is Malaysia, Singapore and Sumatra though it has to be said that the original flora and fauna of the island of Singapore has been drastically affected by industrial development. The extent to which the remaining land is affected by industrial exploitation means that it is very doubtful whether this species still survives there. The chocolate gourami is found principally in slow flowing, densely overgrown watercourses with

Sphaerichthys osphromenoides osphromenoides.

very soft, acidic water, low in minerals. The view put forward by J. REICHELT in 1906 indicating that their preferred waters had a high salt content has since been invalidated by recent findings and the results of keeping them in captivity.

At the time REICHELT wrote:

"In July I was in Sumatra for the third time. When I caught this species of fish in ditches and ponds some six to ten miles

Asiatic distribution of *Sphaerichthys osphrome-noides osphromenoides*.

from the coast, it had never occurred to me that the water there could be even higher in salt content. The water in the ditches was as dark as black coffee and it was only after repeated filtering that you could get it to the colour of light beer. The inhabitants here filter all their drinking water and at the point of consumption it still has that darkish hue typical of a Bavarian beer. All in all, I could not have guessed how high the salt content of the water there was, yet the native population, both Malays and Chinese, regard it as pure, fresh water."

For the

general care

of this species there are some special factors that have to be borne in mind. In order to guarantee a certain degree of "water

stability" the aquaria should not be too small, so that a length upwards of 80 cm and a depth of 40 cm, with plenty of plants is recommended. These fish should be kept only with their own kind or with other small, very peaceable species.

The water values should be as low as possible with a general and carbonate hardness of 2—3° and a pH of 5.5 to 6. Where your starting water is too hard, you can achieve these values by using a total desalination plant, also known as an artificial resin ion exchanger. These items of equipment can be obtained from pet shops and specialist aquarium dealers. Where the tap water is soft to medium hard the same effect can also be achieved by thorough filtering over active peat. For 100 liters of water where the water values are around 10° general and carbonate hardness, about two packets of active peat will be needed to bring the values down to this level. Continuous filtering should then be provided over active peat in order to keep the water stable. The "added ingredients" that arise incidentally out of the use of the peat are a welcome side benefit.

The light brown coloration is not quite equivalent to the "black coffee" effect described by J. REICHELT for the natural biotope — but it does look like a glass of decent beer!

The water temperature should be around the 28 °C mark, though this can rise to 30 °C at times. With these high temperatures and the low mineral content of the water, it is also important to select the right plants because not all species fulfill the requirements and can tolerate these extreme values. Suitable plants would be *Rotala macranda, Alternanthera sessilis, Hygrophila polysperma*, the Indian water star, as well as *Cryptocoryne walkeri* and *Cryptocoryne petchii*. To promote healthy plant growth crypto fertilizers are recommended, a standard ion combination that employs a new technique for releasing the right nutrients into the water since aquatic plants will only do well if properly fed. The old maxim still holds: Healthy plant growth equals "healthy" water and this is the crucial factor if chocolate gouramis are to be kept with any hope of success. The plants should be set out in informal decorative groups with the tall stemmed plants at the back and the lower growing cryptocorynes at the front. One or two pieces of bogwood could form the remaining decorative features. The aquarium should have a dark background and stand in a quiet part of the room. In this case it is advisable to diverge from the standard lighting strength of 0.5 Watts per liter and allow 1 Watt per liter as the peat-filtered water is quite brown and absorbs so much of the light. In this way you can ensure that the plants get enough light. Gravel with a grain size up to 3 mm should be used for the bed and the aquarium should be covered with a pane of glass to avoid cooling of the air just above the water surface.

An aquarium set up in the manner described above is ideally suited for

breeding,

though it must be said that successes have been few and far between. J. REICHELT wrote in 1906 about what he still considered to be his live-bearing gouramis and which led him to the following conclusion, despite his transport difficulties: "As a rule all the ailing gourami females each produced 25 to 40 youngsters before they died. The young always looked the same as the old ones, that is to say, equally colourful." Nowadays we know that the fish is not a live bearer but a mouth brooder. This must imply that at the time they found their way into Herr REICHELT's net these females must have been holding fertilized eggs or even larvae in their mouths.

As a basis for a reasonably successful shot at breeding, you should acquire about 20 specimens and bring them up to breeding condition with a good, varied diet.

As *Spaerichthys o. osphromenoides* are not bubble nest builders, the spawning process is generally preceded by a courthsip display involving much spreading of fins and mutual circling near the bottom of the tank and usually amongst plants in some quiet corner of the aquarium. Hans-Joachim RICHTER gave a very good description

of the whole procedure in 1972 which he portrays graphically: "The actual act of spawning can be recognised by the fact that the whole body of the male starts to quiver after it has swum inside the loop formed by the curvature of the female's body. Spawning takes place shortly afterwards, the usual number of eggs being in the region of 80. The pair will then swim next to one another for a while before the female starts to gather up the eggs a few seconds later. The throat pouch soon becomes very distended with the weight of the eggs. She then swims to a darker nook in the aquarium where she holds up until the eggs hatch."

Luckily I have been able to observe this behaviour and the associated mouth brooding care on a number of occasions. In doing so I ascertained that the females release their young after around 19 days at a water temperature of around 27 °C. The tiny *Sphaerichthys o. osphromenoides* then have an average total length of 6.7 mm, measurements having been carried out on several specimens. The sizes varied between 6.5 and 6.9 mm. There was no longer any sign of the yolk sac. The youngsters were already very similar in colour to the parents, namely chocolate brown with the occasional markings made up of dark red spots. A light, almost transparent to light yellow ring ran around the middle of the body. The dorsal and anal fins were likewise already a deep shade of brown. In relation to their size the young fish had a small mouth. Despite this, they immediately started taking newly hatched nauplii of *Artemia salina* as their first food. So long as they are fed at frequent intervals and are given good quality water they will grow well. they can reach a length of 15 mm after just three weeks, by which time they will have taken on a distinctly higher body shape and almost acquired the same silhouette as their parents. The brood developed successfully with water values of 60 to 95 microsiemens on average with a pH of between 5 and 6.3. Clean water is important. Water temperatures were usually 27 or 28 °C, anything warmer being unnecessary in my opinion.

A short time ago a description of a new sub species of the well-known chocolate gourami was put forward, this being

◆ *Sphaerichthys osphrome-noides selatanensis*
(VIERKE, 1979)

which differs from the previous species by virtue of having fewer hard rays in the dorsal and anal fins and in the shape and size of the lower gill cover. Overall the head is somewhat smaller and in relation to it the eyes are bigger. According to the original description, differences in colour include the light longitudinal stripe and an additional light transverse stripe that starts at the front end of the dorsal fin and terminates behind the ventral fin. At first glance one might compare this coloration with the well-known alarm colouring of the chocolate gourami.

The total length of this new sub species is given as barely 5 cm.

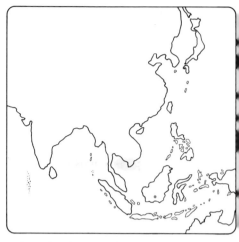

Asiatic distribution of *Sphaerichthys osphrome-noides selatanensis.*

Its

natural habitat
is to be found in the area in the direct vicinity of Banjarmasin in the south east of

Borneo. Its care requires the same conditions as for *Spaerichthys o. osphromenoides.* In this species too the female undertakes the mouth brooding duties.

Sphaerichthys osphromenoides selatanensis.

The large, very placid and easily kept group of fish from the

Trichogaster genus

stand out because of their particularly magnificent colouring. One of the most beautiful species is

▶ *Trichogaster leeri* 4³/₄"
(BLEEKER, 1861)

Asiatic distribution of *Trichogaster leeri*.

also known as the pearl or mosaic gourami.

It grows up to 12 cm long. The males have a glowing red colouring on their gills, breast and belly which extends to the thread-like ventral fins and the front half of the anal fin. Apart from this the male has a pointed dorsal fin which is more rounded and less long in the female. The females also lack the red colouring of the males. Unfortunately, the sexes are only distinguishable when the fish have reached a length of 8 cm or more, which is the equivalent of seven month old specimens.

Trichogaster leeri.

127

The
natural habitat
of *Trichogaster leeri* has been stated as Thailand, Malaysia, Sumatra and Borneo, though Thailand seems to me to be questionable. In spite of numerous attempts, I have never managed to find any of these fish there. Nor do they occur in any abundance in Malaysia. They live to some extent in slowly flowing waters around 30 cm deep that carry clear, soft and acidic water. As their favourite territories are often jungle waters, they are found much of the time in semi-darkness.

For their
general care
this species should be given large aquaria, i. e tanks upwards of 130 cm long by 50 cm wide and 50 cm deep and, if possible, even bigger. These should be well planted with lots of hideouts amongst pieces of bogwood and tall-growing clumps of plants like *Hygrophila stricta, Hygrophila corymbosa* and a bush, say 10 to 15 stems, of *Hydrocotyle leucocephala,* a South American plant that generally requires water temperatures up to 25 °C but which can grow in conditions up to 27 °C. Between these, in an open area, *Nymphaea lotus,* an African lily with a reddish hue, will form a good contrast to the green plants. Their late-developing floating leaves make a favourite shelter for the fish. As the mosaic gourami is a very peaceable sort, indeed even timid, it should not be kept in the company of aggressive subjects. Recommended companions are smaller dwarf cichlids as fish for the bottom zone, together with other labyrinth fish and perhaps also a shoal of 10 to 15 small characins. But do be careful with barbs! Not all species of these are suitable companions for these gouramis because they like to nibble away at the thread-like extensions to the ventral fins of *Trichogaster leeri* and this kind of behaviour can lead to some nasty wounds. The temperature should be around 25 °C and it would be advantageous if the water could be soft and slightly acidic. The aquarium must be lit in the normal way which is to say at 0.5 Watts per liter. Ideally, the conditions you

give your mosaic gouramis should reflect those outlined in the earlier section on the "large aquarium for labyrinth fish".

For
breeding
them it is absolutely vital that they have an aquarium 100 cm long, or better still 130 cm. You may succeed in a smaller aquarium but there are many drawbacks involved. One is that the pair that you put in there could react to one another with great timidity and, furthermore, if they do produce young, the space available to accommodate the crop of youngsters, often in excess of 700, is inadequate.

For successful breeding the water values should not be more than 2 ° dH for general and carbonate hardness. If your starting water is hardish or contains a high level of minerals, you can achieve these figures by mixing in clean rainwater if you can collect some or better with chemically desalinated water. This operation is done with a complete desalination plant obtainable from your specialist dealer.

These values can be checked in seconds using the tetraTest GH, TetraTest KH and TetraTest pH kits. If the starting water is not too hard or too rich in minerals, then filtering over active peat will suffice. The brown discoloration of the water that will then arise bears a close resemblance to their natural conditions. For breeding purposes the water temperature must be raised to 30 °C. Several groups of plants should be put in to grow to the water surface where the depth is 25 cm. The open areas in between should partly be filled in with floating plants like *Ceratopteris pteridoides* or *Pistia stratiotes.* The aquarium must be covered with a glass pane and weakly lit until mating has occurred and thereafter normally.

One or two Tetra Brillant filters installed in the corners will ensure clear water and a light movement of the water in parts. The male *Trichogaster leeri* will then build his bubble nest amongst or under the floating plants and the female will also be able to find some refuge in the zone with water movement if his attentions become too ardent.

A very slim, streamlined representative of this genus is

▶ *Trichogaster microlepis*
(GUNTHER, 1861)

6"

also known as the moonlight gourami.

This species can grow to about 15 cm long and is considered to be a very placid variety. There are distinct colour differences between the sexes. In fully grown males the whole body is covered by a silvery green hue and they also have a delicate red breast and reddish ventral fins that are drawn out into thread-like extensions. They have a longish dorsal fin that grows out to a pointed tip. The females are a silvery colour and have a short, rounded dorsal fin.

The
natural habitat
is Thailand and the adjacent eastern and south eastern regions. They do not occur with the abundance of the other *Trichogaster* species. They are found in the klongs in towns and in the countryside, both in gently flowing and standing water, under a variety of environmental conditions in areas of high vegetation and also in large lakes like, for instance, Lake Ahn Sabadu near Ampo Sikju, a water reservoir measuring 100×300 m and up to 2 m deep. In this water there were some rafts of a species of *Elodea* about 3 m^2 in size growing on a gravel bed with a grain size of up to 2 mm.

Trichogaster microlepis.

Asiatic distribution of *Trichogaster microlepis*.

Table No. 5

Locality:	Lake Ahn Sabudu near Ampo Sikju 46 km before Nakhon Racha-sima in the direc-tion of the Cam-bodian border
Clarity:	clear
Colour:	none
pH value:	7.3
D general hardness	4 °dH
D carbonate hardness	3 °dH
Conductivity:	120 microsiemens at 27 °C
Nitrite:	0.05 mg/l
Water depth:	up to 200 cm
Water movement:	none
Water temperature:	27 °C
Date of tests:	11. 11. 1977
Time:	17.30

Trichogaster microlepis was found living here in the company of *Chanda ranga,* the Indian glassfish and *Betta splendens,* the wild form of the Siamese fighting fish. As this lake has a number of broad feeder chan-nels originating from the surrounding rice paddies, it is likely that these fish also migrate to the rice fields and their klongs.

The
general care
of these fish is straightforward. You need only give them an aquarium upwards of 100 cm long by 50 cm wide and 50 cm deep, plenty of suitable plants and a quiet location. As this species is also somewhat timid, fish with a pacific, non-aggressive nature should be chosen as fellow tenants. Dwarf cichlids, characins and other labyrinth fish are also suitable companions for this fish. The water temperature should be between 26 and 28 °C. Floating plants or those with surface leaves such as *Nymphaea* us, in both the green and red leaved form, whose leaves will spread to cover large areas of the surface, are good subjects for normal care conditions. Otherwise all the recommendations for the "large aquarium for labyrinth fish" apply here. As with all other species of labyrinth fish, I would remind you that a regular water change every fortnight, replacing about a quarter to a third of the aquarium content, is of prime importance.

Similarly, for
breeding
this species a tank of suitable size should be made available. The minimum length must be 100 cm with the tank being set up as for general care since you can reckon on *Tricho-gaster microlepis* producing more than 1000 offspring at one go. At spawning time it is best if the breeding tank is kept in semi darkness.

The male builds his bubble nest at the surface. It is reinforced with bits of plants and can reach quite a size, often rising 2 cm or so over the surface of the water. The young fish are swimming around after about four days at a water temperature of 29 °C and need to be given copious amounts of food. At this point it is probably best to remove the parents from the aquarium. A suitable first food is Tetra MikroMin, a flaked food that is specially formulated to cover the nutritional requirements of young fish. It should be given several times a day in amounts that are small enough to be eaten in a short time.

Another very interesting species is
▶ *Trichogaster pectoralis*
(REGAN, 1909)

6"

the snake-skinned gourami.

This species generally grows to 15 cm long and the sexes are easy to tell apart by the shape of the dorsal fin which is rounded in the female and pointed and more elongated in the male. Their pattern of transverse bands is always clearly visible in spite of any changes in mood in these fish.

The
natural habitat
is Thailand, Cambodia and Malaysia but because of its suitability for exploitation as a commercial fish, escapees have extended its range to areas such as Sri Lanka which could nowadays be classed as the home of this species. Here they live in the lowlands at the fringes of low hills in the interior of the country where rice paddies seem to dominate the landscape. In fact, these watery fields offer a home to many kinds of fish.

Asiatic distribution of *Trichogaster pectoralis*.

Narrow channels, 1 m wide and up to 80 cm deep, supply the fields with water and constitute an ideal irrigation system for rice cultivation. In these paddies the temperatures often soar to 37 °C during periods of intense sunshine. At such times the fish withdraw to

Trichogaster pectoralis.

Table No. 6

Locality:	Rice field near Mahawewa, 19 miles north of Negombo, Sri Lanka
Clarity:	clear
Colour:	light brownish
pH value:	5.8
D general hardness	4 °dH
D carbonate hardness	6 °dH
Conductivity:	250 microsiemens at 37 °C
Nitrite:	0.05 mg/l
Water depth:	up to 5 cm
Water movement:	none
Water temperature:	37 °C
Date of tests:	17. 3. 1975
Time:	16.30

The water channels surrounding paddies are often a home to *Trichogaster pectoralis*.

there is often a large number of fish to be found there, some of which, being about 15 cm long with a body depth of 5 cm, seem to be "standing" in the water. They are often seen lying on their side or leaping over the muddy, sandy slicks of soil until they reach the next decent water hollow.

The
general care
of these fish is straightforward. However, you should bear in mind that they require plenty of room and need an aquarium size upwards of 100 cm long. The "large aquarium for labyrinth fish" could be regarded as ideal for this species. Nor are these fish demanding in terms of water values. The normal water temperature should be between 25 and 28 °C. It is a placid sort and gets along well with smaller fish.

Breeding
this species is only possible in adequately-sized aquaria. The dimensions for breeding tanks must be at least 130 cm long by 40 cm wide and 30 cm deep. The provision of lots of well planted zones in a bed of gravel with 3 mm grain size, or even without any bed material, combined with weak lighting and a water temperature of around 30 °C, will guarantee successful breeding. It should not be overlooked that this species can be rather shy and so the aquarium needs to be stood in a quiet corner. The male builds a bubble nest at the water surface. *Trichogaster pectoralis* is a prolific sort and over 1000 offspring are not uncommon. A proven hit as a first food for these youngsters is Tetra MikroMin, a fine powdered food containing amongst other things a lot of green leaf matter and marine algae. This should be strewn on the surface serveral times a day in amounts that the fish will consume in minutes. It can also be given in the form of a "liquid feed" in very small amounts every two hours or so. If there is good aeration in the tank such as produced by an air stone, its proper distribution throughout the aquarium will be assured.

the cooler waters of the branches of the supply system. Often the water level in the fields is only some 5 cm deep but even so

A very widespread species which has become a very interesting variety in the last few years as a result of the numerous hybrid forms is

▶ *Trichogaster trichopterus trichopterus*
(PALLAS, 1777)

6"

the two-spot gourami.

This species grows up to about 15 cm long and is characterised by a beautiful pattern of gold spots on the anal fins which is also present to some extent on the dorsal and anal fins. The two dark spots, one in the middle of the body and the other on the caudal peduncle have given this fish its English name. The sexes are very easy to tell apart. When spawning time approaches the females develop a pronounced swelling of the girth around the breast and have a shorter, more rounded dorsal fin, in contrast to that of the male which is longer and more pointed.

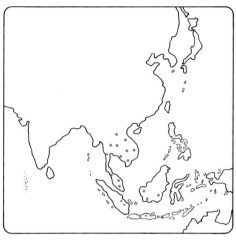

Asiatic distribution of *Trichogaster trichopterus trichopterus*.

Trichogaster trichopterus trichopterus.

133

Table No. 7

Locality:	Forest stream near Kuantan, Malaysia
Clarity:	cloudy
Colour:	yellowish/silty
pH value:	5.4
D general hardness	under 1 °dH
D carbonate hardness	under 1 °dH
Conductivity:	22 microsiemens at 25 °C
Nitrite:	0.00 mg/l
Water depth:	up to 60 cm
Water movement:	gently flowing
Water temperature:	25 °C
Date of tests:	19. 11. 1977
Time:	12.00

Table No. 8

Locality:	Paddy field, western side Penang Island, Malaysia
Clarity:	clear
Colour:	none
pH value:	6.5
D general hardness	under 1 °dH
D carbonate hardness	under 1 °dH
Conductivity:	50 — 100 microsiemens at 33 °C
Nitrite:	0.00 mg/l
Water depth:	to 5 cm on average
Water movement:	none
Water temperature:	33 °C; 28 °C at a depth of 40 cm in the klong linked to this field.
Date of tests:	28. 11. 1977
Time:	11.00

The
natural habitat
extends over a wide range, covering Thailand, Cambodia, Vietnam, Malaysia, Sumatra, Singapore, Borneo and many of the surrounding islands. They are commercially farmed. They can be caught equally in the big cast nets in the klongs of Bangkok or in little watercourses in such places as Kuantan on the South China sea in Malaysia. Just as the diner in a restaurant in our latitudes might be able to select from a tank full of live trout, in Malaysian restaurants it is the two-spot gourami that is displayed as the potential fish course. They are shown swimming in big, glass bowls until someone chooses them to be served grilled or fried.

Farmers in Thailand like to set up their holding as an island house in a sea of paddy fields. The house is bordered by a klong or canal which serves in the first place as a sort of protective "garden wall" and secondly, as a doorstep "larder". The widest possible variety of species is kept in these private, domestic klongs. As well as *Trichogaster trichopterus trichopterus* one finds *Trichogaster pectoralis, Anabas testidineus* and also the wild form of the Siamese fighting fish. *Trichogaster trichopterus trichopterus* and

T. pectoralis often build their bubble nests just a few centimeters apart amongst the submerged and sometimes semi-emergent vegetation of these canals. As the water is usually quite cloudy with the amount of silt in it, these fish cannot see more than a short distance ahead of themselves. Their bubble nests may rise up more than 3 cm above the

A bubble nest amongst emergent plants in the natural biotope of the two-spot gourami.

surface and are up to 25 cm long so that they are often subjected to the full strength of the sun's rays. It seems that one of the functions of the bubbles under these circumstances, i.e. in temperatures of around 33 °C, is to shield the brood against overheating. At varying intervals the water is let out of the klongs and the larger specimens are harvested. Any of them that are not used right away are gutted, decapitated and left to dry in the sun on a wicker mat. Two-spot gouramis are found everywhere. They live in flowing watercourses but also, perhaps more frequently, in small and large stretches of water where they find their favourite biotope amongst the luxuriant underwater vegetation. They are not at all fussed about water quality. The temperatures in their natural habitat vary between 25 and 30 °C.

Consequently, their
general care
can only be described as unproblematical. An appropriate size for the aquarium would be upwards of 100 cm long by 50 cm wide and deep. A smaller tank could be used but is not recommended. The set up as described for the "large aquarium for laby-

rinth fish" might be considered ideal. The two-spot gourami should be kept in a relatively quiet position, in a tank decorated with groups of plants and pieces of bogwood. It should be lit in the standard way and have a water temperature of around 25 °C.

Aquaria that have the above facilities are also suitable for
breeding
As this species is very productive, large tanks are advantageous. Granted, I have seen two-spot gouramis spawning in aquaria 40 cm long and 30 cm wide but this must be a real torment for the breeding pair and youngsters alike. Ardent males are occasionally capable of biting off the anal fin of the female and unless she is offered a sufficient number of escape routes, she may have to endure some painful consequences of his attentions. When raising a brood that may be in excess of 1000, a larger amount of water may be biologically more stable and, moreover, offers the fry more swimming space. The male builds his bubble nest amongst plants floating on the water surface and it may reach a diameter of up to 25 cm.

Two-spot gouramis on display as part of a "live" menu in a restaurant in Malaysia.

Trichogaster trichopterus trichopterus survive drought periods in these water holes.

A subspecies of Trichogaster trichopterus is

▶ *Trichogaster trichopterus sumatranus*
(LADIGES, 1933)

also known as the blue gourami. 4³/4"

This is a rather smaller variety that is fully grown at 12 cm long. Its very beautiful blue colouring distinguishes it from the two-spot gourami which is more of a bluish grey. Sexual differentiation is again based on the size of the girth of females that are ready to spawn and the fact that the males have a longer dorsal fin that extends into a pointed tip.

Asiatic distribution of *Trichogaster trichopterus sumatranus.*

Trichogaster trichopterus sumatranus.

136

The
natural habitat
of this fish is areas of Sumatra where it is endemic.

Its
general care
is practically the same as for the preceding species, save for the fact that a more satisfactory average value for the water temperature would be 27 °C. Once again, the appropriate form of aquarium is the "large aquarium for labyrinth fish".

Nor is
breeding
very difficult. Regular checking of the water values will prove useful as this subspecies prefers soft, slightly acidic water. *Trichogaster trichopterus sumatranus* is not quite as prolific but a large breeding tank is advisable all the same. The water temperature should be around 30 °C and a good filtration system, using a Brilliant Filter as an internal unit — also usable as a highly efficient double filter — will ensure clear, clean water. This is an important criterion for guaranteeing the sort of conditions in which the young fish will thrive.

Over the last few years a number of other special hybrid forms of *Trichogaster t. trichopterus* have won a good deal of popularity in aquarist circles. For instance, one of the best loved of these is the "Cosby" variety which carries very pretty, dark blue markings that contrast nicely with the ground colour, especially in the juveniles. Unfortunately, this becomes less distinct as the fish becomes older.

Another hybrid form is the "golden gourami", a variant of the two-spot gourami that has, as the name indicates, a very beautiful intense gold colouring. The third popular hybrid form is known as the "silver gourami", a colour sport that often has a delicate greeny silver or sometimes a reddish silver sheen covering its entire body. All these hybrid forms are somewhat less blessed in terms of natural vitality and vigour than the original type. They often remain smaller and generally weaker and produce fewer young.

Cosby gourami — hybrid form.

Golden gourami — hybrid form.

Silver gourami — hybrid form.

One of the smaller representatives of the labyrinth fish is

▶ *Trichopsis pumilus*
(ARNOLD, 1936)
the croaking gourami.

This fish grows to a length of 4 cm and makes a very amenable member of the aquarium community. It is not always that easy to distinguish between the sexes. The females are less colourful and usually have a rounded anal fin. The safest and most reli- able way of telling the sexes apart is to put them into a little glass container in front of a strong source of light so that this can shine through them after the fashion of an X-ray. This will enable the ovary to be seen in the female, recognisable as a dark shadow at the rear of the body cavity, running in a triangu- lar shape in the direction of the tail. It has to be said though that the appearance of indi- vidual specimens can vary greatly to the extent that many breeding failures can often be attributed to a supposed pair turning out to be two fish of the same sex.

Trichopsis pumilus.

The
natural habitat

is Vietnam, Cambodia, West Malaysia and Thailand. I have caught this species mostly in overgrown, pond-like accumulations of water and in narrow, shallow ditches. In many instances a close cover of floating plants left very little of the water surface open to the light. In the shallower zones of this biotope the water temperature could be as high as 33 °C. The oxygen levels were often very low. Usually these fish were found in the company of *Trichogaster t. trichopterus*, *Trichogaster pectoralis*, *Trichopsis vittatus* and *Anabas testudineus*, for which, however, they seemed to serve as a prey item. The croaking gourami is generally seen in smallish groups of six to ten individuals, often joined by some small examples of two-spot gouramis, up to say 5 cm long.

Asiatic distribution of *Trichopsis pumilus*.

For the
general care

of these little croaking gouramis small aquaria up to 70 cm long are adequate. These should be well planted, containing tall-stemmed plants like *Limnophila aquatica* or *Cabomba aquatica* as well as large-leaved aquatic plants like *Aponogeton echinatus*, the red and green forms of *Nymphaea lotus* and *Hygrophila corymbosa*. As *Trichopsis pumilus* is very fond of placing its bubble nest under leaves, these plants are particu-larly recommended if you want them to breed. The water values are of secondary importance though they should not be too far on the hard or alkaline side. The water temperature should be around 25 °C. The recommended material for the bed is once more gravel with a grain size between 1 and 3 mm. Small cavities in rocks or pieces of bogwood and perhaps an upturned flower pot with a hole knocked out can be incorporated into the decor. The aquarium can be lit in the standard way and should stand in a quiet location.

Breeding

this little species of labyrinth fish is not at all difficult. For this purpose the temperature should be raised to 28 or 30 °C in an aquarium set up in the same way as for their general care. The male usually builds his little bubble nest under leaves or an over-hanging rock or indeed in any nook or cranny that offers a "roof". A male can be mated with one or two females and will divide his attentions between the two of them over the course of several days. During the courtship display of these males and when they are adopting a threat posture, one can often hear croaking or possibly squeaking noises. In spite of its small stature, *Trichopsis pumilus* is very capable of defending its nest against larger fish. In doing so, its rows of shining blue dots make it light up like a little jewel. This species also entwines in a courtship embrace under the bubble nest. Both partners gather up the little batches of eggs as they sink through the water and carry them back to the nest. Once spawning is concluded, it is a good idea if the female is not removed from the breeding tank because her presence there seems to incite the male to take more assiduous care of his brood. After about four days the young fish are swimming and both parents can be taken out of the aquarium.

One of the species that grows to a slightly larger size than the previous one is

▶ *Trichopsis schalleri*
(LADIGES, 1952)

which reaches about 5 cm in length. This species seems to lack the saddle-like depression on the head that is typical of the *Trichopsis* group, giving them a turned-up nose look. They also differ in the form of the spiny rays of the anal fin and in their colouring.

On this LADIGES writes: "In the live fish the longitudinal stripes are chestnut brown, accompanied by intensive greenish blue rows of shimmering scales that can interrupt the upper stripe in a number of places under the dorsal fin. The dorsal fin is edged with a reddish brown hem and the anal fin is similarly bordered by a narrow dark hem."

As such, this species has an appearance that is not that dissimilar from that of *Trichopsis pumilus*. Many authors have recently put forward the viewpoint that this fish does not constitute a species in its own right but is in reality a subspecies of *Trichopsis vitta-*

Trichopsis schalleri.

tus, whose numerous local forms require urgent revision.

I should like to refute this view here and now. For me, *Trichopsis schalleri* is indeed a species in its own right because if it were to occur as a subspecies, it would not continue to exist as a distinct entity where it cohabits the same biotope as *T. vittatus*. I was able to observe and catch *T. schalleri* and *T. vittatus* living together in eight locations that were spread over distances up to 40 km apart. The habitats concerned differed widely from each other. So there is no question of there being any separation on geographical or ecological grounds to back up these claims. The "X-ray" method is recommended as the best way of distinguishing the sexes once again.

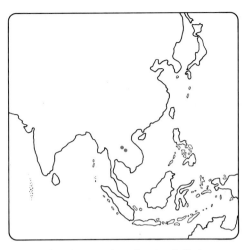

Asiatic distribution of *Trichopsis schalleri*.

The
natural habitat
is stated in the original description to be the district of Nam-Mun near Korat, 135 miles north east of Bangkok in Thailand. Unfortunately, I did not have the good luck to catch this species in the area of the Mun river near the town of Korat (now known as Nakhon Rachasima). But to compensate for this, they swam into my net in great numbers in the more northerly area from Khon Kaen to Nong Khai on the Mekong River, together with *Trichopsis vittatus, Betta smaragdina* and other species. All the above-listed species occurred in the most varied of

habitats — rice paddies, swampy meadowland, klongs and watercourses — especially in the area within a radium of 100 km of the town of Nong Khai. The water temperatures of these biotopes were between 28 and 32 °C. In all cases there was a great deal of plant growth in the bank zones and in many cases the entire expanse of the water was overgrown. Depths varied from 5 to 30 cm.

Their
general care and breeding
are the same as for the other species of *Trichopsis* already mentioned.

This thick clump of tangled aquatic plants in the area of Nong Khai in north eastern Thailand is typical of the favourite habitat of *Betta smaragdina, Trichopsis schalleri* and *Trichopsis vittatus*.

The largest of the three croaking gouramis is

▶ *Trichopsis vittatus*
(CUVIER and VALENCIENNES, 1831)

which reaches a total length of 7 cm. Here too, sexual differentiation is no easy matter. Adult specimens often exhibit a bold, round spot on their shoulder and many authors claim that this is a sure distinguishing feature for males. Unfortunately, females also carry this spot so that it has no real validity as a criterion for sexual differentiation. Large males usually have elongated, pointed fins with a narrow border. But as the geographi-cal forms display quite variable colouring, the safest way of telling the sexes apart in this species is once again the "X-ray" method as described for *Trichopsis pumilus*.

The
natural habitat
comprises pond-like accumulation of water, small rivers, canals, ditches and rice fields. They often live in the very cloudy, dirty waters of urban canals. The distribution of this species is very widespread, covering Sumatra, the Sunda Islands, Malaysia, Thailand and up into Vietnam. They are often to

Trichopsis vittatus.

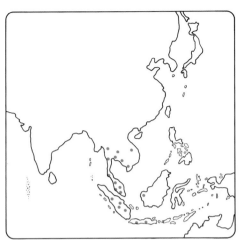

Asiatic distribution of *Trichopsis vittatus*.

point where brood care commences the diameter of the nest may reach 10 cm. During the courtship display one can clearly hear loud croaking sounds that are produced by the male. Mating takes place under the bubble nest and involves the usual ritual embrace. The subsequent procedures for brood care are comparable to those of other species of this genus.

be found in small shoals in the open water between large plant formations or under the floating leaves of aquatic plants.

Their
general care
is easy. You need to give them an aquarium upwards of 70 cm long, 40 cm wide and 40 cm deep with lots of plants. Floating plants such as *Riccia flutans,* the crystal-wort, and *Ceratopteris pteridoides,* the floating fern, are recommended. The water values are of secondary importance. The temperature should be set at 25 °C and lighting provided at the normal rate of 0.5 Watts per liter. As these fish are some-what shy, their tank should be stood in a quiet position and they should only be kept in the company of similarly placid-natured species.

An aquarium following the above guidelines can be used for
breeding
The fish are then put in as pairs and the water temperature needs to be raised to 28 or 30 °C. This large croaking gourami likes to build its bubble nest at the water surface or under the leaves of floating plants. At the

Some of the ponds in which *Trichopsis vittatus* is found hold very cloudy water.

THE AFRICAN LABYRINTH FISH

The concluding part of this book will deal with the climbing perches from tropical Africa that have been given the name "bush fish" by Professor Werner LADIGES. With around 25 species, the genus *Ctenopoma* is the largest of all the labyrinth fish. As has been reported in many publications, these fish are generally timid creatures that lead a retiring yet highly predatory existence. However, if they are properly cared for, this view is quickly refuted. The bush fish are

very interesting subjects for study and can be kept in the aquarium without posing any risk to their fellows provided these are not too small. Any display of aggression towards other species is usually merely defensive behaviour and they are, in fact, rather pleasant fish on the whole. Bush fish could not be rated amongst the most colourful of the labyrinth fish but are nonetheless appealing creatures thanks to their quite unusual body shape.

Catching these fish in the streams of tropical rain forests can often be a tricky business.

144

The species can be divided into two groups, namely one that practises brood care and another that does not i.e. are free spawners. The brood carers build bubble nests, spawn under them and take care of the young until they can swim independently. In this respect they are similar to the Asiatic labyrinth fish. The species that are known to belong to this group are *Ctenopoma ansorgii, Ct. damasi, Ct. fasciolatum, Ct. nanum.* The free spawning species release their milt and eggs in the open water after a brief courtship embrace, often just a few centimeters from the bottom and without any prior nest building or subsequent brood care. Once again, with the reservation "as far as is known", we can say that about half the species of *Ctenopoma* that have been observed live in captivity and could be persuaded to breed have proved to belong to this group, including *Ct. acutirostre (?), Ct. argentoventer, Ct. kingsleyae, Ct. multispinis (?), Ct. muriei, Ct. ocellatum (?)* and *Ct. oxythynchum.*

Sexual differentiation is generally not difficult with the brood caring species. Here the differences in colour and fin shape make it easy to tell the males from the females. However, things are very different when it comes to the free spawning species. In this context Professor Hans M. PETERS came to some quite remarkable conclusions based on a study of *Ct. kingsleyae.* In contrast to the brood carers, those species that have been closely watched in captivity have some rather peculiar features. These are small areas of scales the edges of which are not equipped with little teeth on the back edge but with relatively long spines.

One of these patches is found just behind the eyes and the other on either side of the caudal peduncle. These features are found in male specimens but can also be seen, though to a lesser extent, in sub adult females. It seems that these patches of scales assist the male in grasping the female during their brief embrace that forms part of the mating ritual. Exceptions to this general rule, as Dr. Sylvia BERNS discovered in her laboratory experiments, are the fast swimming, "stretched" species of *Ctenopoma* such as *Ct. multispinis, Ct. machadoi, Ct. nigropannosum* and *Ct. pellegrinii.* These species only possess the spiny patch of scales at their front end. Although it has not yet been possible to observe the breeding behaviour of the species just listed, it can be assumed that these too are free spawners.

The patches of scales mentioned above should not be confused with the normal *Ctenoid* scales — the comb-like scales of the bush fish — that are normal features of these fish. Similarly, the strong teeth on the rear edge of the gill cover should be regarded separately, these being the weapons that can cause nasty injuries when catching these fish with a hand net. This is another thing to bear in mind if you are considering keeping any of these *Ctenopoma* species.

Bush fish have a very healthy appetite and copious amounts of high grade food must be fed to them, especially the larger species. Yet they are also happy to eat flaked food. In their natural habitat most species live in clear, clean, often flowing water.

In the course of my frequent trips to west Africa I found time and again that these fish live predominantly in oxygen-rich, acidic water that is low in minerals and with a temperature of between 24 and 28 °C. Rather more infrequently, they can be encountered in the warm, open bushland waters which are usually low in oxygen. Unfortunately, dealers do not often stock these *Ctenopoma* species. We live in the hope that this situation might soon change so that the genus will be available to amateurs who will then be able to help out in clearing up some of the unresolved questions relating to these interesting creatures.

One of the lesser known species is

▶ *Ctenopoma acutirostre*
(PELLEGRIN, 1899)
the spotted climbing perch.

The English name for this fish only gives an indication of what this fish looks like and tells us nothing about its behaviour. So to deal with its appearance first: in a sense it has almost a leopard-like appearance, with dark brown to black spots of irregular shape and size on a yellowy buff to light brown background. Only the pectoral fins and the trailing edge of the caudal, dorsal and anal fins are transparent and colourless. The fish are slow growers but eventually reach a length of 15 cm. They will only attain this size in a spacious aquarium and after two to three years. *Ctenopoma acutirostre* should usually be obtained as juvenile specimens. They are often available through dealers at a length of some 4 cm and soon settle down well in the home aquarium. This adaptability

Ctenopoma acutirostre.

is significant because most of the fish on offer are caught in the wild. They also adapt quite readily to different water values. One conspicuous feature of their appearance are the large eyes which indicate crepuscular or nocturnal habits. In fact they do become more active towards evening, in contrast to their behaviour throughout the day when they spend much of their time concealed or almost motionless in the water. Their deep-cut mouth turns into a large oval suction tube when they pounce on their prey and the object disappears "down the hatch" in the blink of an eyelid. For this reason it is not a good idea to keep small species of fish in a community tank with the spotted climbing perch.

If this species is kept in a well-planted aquarium with an adequate provision of bogwood and caves, it will soon overcome its natural shyness. Nor do they prove to be all that predacious in their behaviour. In fact, the opposite is true and they can be quite retiring. With the right care, in the company of fish that are wont to swim around in the open water, they may become rather confiding and start to spend a lot of time near the front pane of the tank, often giving the impression that they are begging for food. Their enormous body depth and massive head give them a very impressive appearance. At times their decorative spotted markings give way to a dirty brown basic coloration that makes it difficult to make them out against the decaying leaves of plants. This camouflage is clearly a big help when they are hunting. If they wander into a territory that is occupied by other fish, they are only recognised and repelled after a little time. When they are spotted, they never react aggressively but simply slip away from the attentions of the other fish and vanish into the background like a drifting leaf.

They should be given a nutritious diet, including large-flaked foods such as Tetra-Marin and food tablets like Tetra TabiMin. TetraTips FD scattered on the surface is also an important dietary supplement.

The home of these fish is the catchment area of the River Congo in Zaire. This

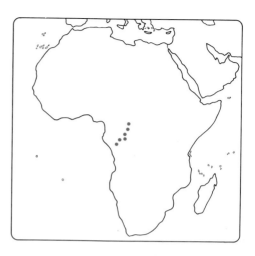

Asiatic distribution of *Ctenopoma acutirostre*.

includes the areas around the Stanley Pool, the vicinity of the towns of Kinshasa and Brazzaville, the Stanley Falls and various tributaries. They live in waters that are fast flowing but also occur in quiet stretches. They are usually to be found in cavities, under overhanging banks or amongst dense, tangled plant formations. Up till now, these fish have only been caught at night when they have left the protection of their hideouts.

The water values of their biotopes are known from a variety of reports. On average, the recorded general hardness levels have been from 2 to 3° dH and the pH from 7 to 7.5. Water temperatures are stated as being 25 to 29 °C. We can also conclude from these reports that they should be kept in water with the lowest possible mineral content. Although this might be of secondary importance for normal care, it may well be significant for successful breeding. Unfortunately, we do not have any accounts of the latter and it remains an important objective for the future. However, these fish are charming subjects for study in their own right and will hold their fascination over a period of years. The form of aquarium that best suits their requirements is that of the "large aquarium for labyrinth fish".

The next *Ctenopoma* species in this section is the little, 8 cm long, very beautifully coloured

▶ *Ctenopoma ansorgii*
(BOULENGER, 1912)

This climbing perch is regarded as the most splendid of all the species of *Ctenopoma* thanks to its magnificent colouring that is displayed to especially good advantage at different times. It is mostly a beautiful orange brown colour with a hint of a green sheen on the sides of the body and six bold, dark brown transverse stripes. The male also has a white edge to its fins. It is one of the more placid species of climbing perch and makes a very good companion for other labyrinth fish.

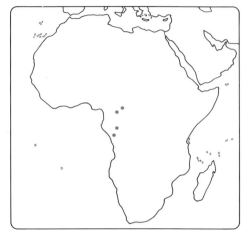

African distribution of *Ctenopoma ansorgii*.

Its

natural habitat
is found predominantly in the great rain forest areas stretching from the Gaboon through Congo-Brazzaville and down into the regions of central Africa, including the Shiloanga river system in Zaire. Other areas in which they have been found are the tributaries of the Ntem and Ogowe river systems south of Djoum.

Here these fish live mainly in the overgrown bank zones of narrow streams, though

Ctenopoma ansorgii.

they are not exactly common anywhere. They seem to occur very erratically and their range appears to be restricted to a few widely scattered localities. The water values in their biotopes are in the acidic range with a low mineral content.

Table No. 9

Locality:	3 km south of the town of Doum, South Cameroon
Clarity:	clear
Colour:	brownish
pH value:	6.4
D general hardness	under 1 °dH
D carbonate hardness	under 1 °dH
Conductivity:	20 microsiemens at 25 °C
Nitrite:	0.00 mg/l
Water depth:	up to 80 cm
Water movement:	gently flowing
Water temperature:	25 °C
Date of tests:	19. 2. 1979
Time:	11.00

Ct. nanum, a similar species, and *Ct. maculatum,* a species with a deeper body form, have been caught living in parallel or adjacent habitats to these fish. The water temperature there is around 25 °C, these habitats being mostly forest streams in deep shade with a low light factor. They are not difficult to keep in an aquarium. If you manage to catch half-grown specimens then the matter of acclimatising them to aquarium conditions is that much easier. It is only adult *Ct. ansorgii* that have trouble settling into the home aquarium and have a habit of dying, to the despair of their keepers and despite their best attentions. However, the specimens on offer at your dealers will usually be captive-bred and thus well used to our conditions. It must be said that you often have to look long and hard before you can spot them in a dealer's tank, so well do they blend in to their surroundings.

Ctenopoma ansorgii is one of the species that cares for its brood. For breeding pur-

poses they must be given a well-planted tank with subdued lighting. The very soft, slightly acidic water must be well filtered and its temperature set at 26 °C. The male builds his bubble nest under the floating plants and the pair will spawn under this structure after performing their courtship routine. The male looks after the brood. Depending on the behaviour of particular individuals, it may be advisable to remove the parent fish after just a day so that the fry can develop unhindered. Once the young are swimming freely, after about four days, they will happily take Tetra MikroMin scattered on the surface.

The little *Ctenopoma ansorgii* start to show their characteristic transverse stripes at the age of around 25 days and by six weeks old they are practising threat postures and mock battles. If well fed on a high-vitamin, growth-promoting flaked food regime, the fish will reach a length of some 6 cm in six months time. *Ctenopoma ansorgii* may be kept in either the "small" or "large" version of labyrinth fish tanks.

Soil tests carried out on the beds of the watercourses in South Cameroon showed a gravel size of up to 2 mm, putting it in the very fine-grained class.

149

One of the more robust climbing perches is

▶ *Ctenopoma argentoventer*
(SCHREITMULLER and AHL, 1922)

In German this fish is called the "silvery" climbing perch but unfortunately this feature is seldom seen and even then only on the throat and belly area in juvenile specimens. In adults this colour changes more to a yellowish golden brown. Its main colouring is a mid to dark brown, with a black fleck of variable intensity and occasionally with a yellowish border on the caudal peduncle. These "silvery" climbing perches grow to 15 cm long. Sexual differentiation is easy in young specimens. Juvenile males have two yellowish transverse stripes on a dark brown body. The one runs from the front part of the dorsal fin over the belly as far as the anal region, in a similar way to juvenile *Ctenopoma maculatum*. At a later stage it is possible to differentiate the sexes by means of the patches of scales behind the eyes and on the caudal peduncle, as

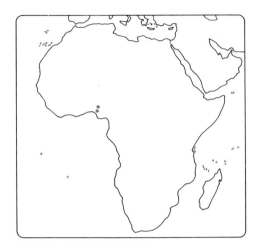

African distribution of *Ctenopoma argentoventer.*

described in detail in the introductory notes on climbing perches.

This species was imported to Germany for the first time in 1912. Its distribution seems to be confined to the region around the Niger delta in Nigeria, one of the known

This is a photograph of *Ctenopoma argentoventer*, though according to TEUGELS & NORRIS 1990 it is a new species *Ctenopoma nebulosum* and as for specimens caught by Heiko BLEHER, it is a *Ct. spec.* from a tributary of the Lua river in the Ubangi catchment area in northern Zaire.

localities for it being "Warri on the lower Niger".

Table No. 10

Locality:	Jamieson River, near the town of Sapele, southern Nigeria (Niger River delta)
Clarity:	very clear
Colour:	dark
pH value:	5.7
D general hardness	under 1 °dH
D carbonate hardness	under 1 °dH
Conductivity:	5 microsiemens at 28.5 °C
Nitrite:	0.00 mg/l
Water depth:	up to 3 m
Water movement:	fast flowing, up to 0.5 m/sec
Water temperature:	28.5 °C
Date of tests:	26. 3. 1978
Time:	15.30

The river water values are comparable with those of the surrounding areas near Sapete and Benin City. The rivers here are the Etiops and the Jamieson. They carry very soft and clean water. They are 80 m wide and flowing.

Another climbing perch found in this area is *Ct. kingsleyae*.

Ctenopoma argentoventer has gained something of a reputation as a bit of a "bad lad" — a fearsome predator, quarrelsome and a biter. I cannot agree with this assessment. My observations have confirmed that this fish is indeed not coy when it comes to taking care of itself in the occasional aquarium disputes and certainly knows how to ensure it has its fair share of the available food. However, it does not seem to be the instigator of arguments and biting matches. These fish should be given a spacious aquarium, with a length in excess of 130 or, better still, 160 cm with a width and height both over 50 cm. A good stock of plants, with clumps reaching up to the surface in

parts, should be provided. The water temperature can be between 23 and 25 °C and the aquarium should be lit at the normal recommended rate of 0.5 Watts per liter. A secure cover should be provided using a number of panes, as this fish is a prodigious jumper. Strong water movement through a motor filter will appeal to them too. For such large fish, tablet food like Tetra TabiMin or scattered TetraTips FD are an essential part of the diet.

Breeding

is thought to have been successful on a number of occasions. As free spawners, they release their eggs into the open water after a brief courtship embrace. These then rise to the surface where they become lodged amongst floating plants and continue to develop. The embryos hatch after 48 hours and the young fish are free swimming two days later. If possible, *Ctenopoma argentoventer* should be kept with fish of the same size so as to keep any potential aggressive tendencies within normal bounds. They should only be housed in a tank set up in accordance with the guidelines for the "large aquarium for labyrinth fish".

Iron sedimentation on the bank of the Etiops river in Nigeria.

A very rare species of the *Ctenopoma* group
— and one that is remarkable for its small
size — was only imported a few years ago by
Dr. Sylvia BERNS and Professor H. M.
PETERS. It is

◗ *Ctenopoma damasi*
(POLL, 1939)

The males of this species reach a total length
of about 7 cm whilst the females are fully
grown at a little over 6 cm. The normal colouring in both sexes is a weak greyish
brown. Dominant males take on a deep
greeny blue colour on a dark body and during courtship and mating they turn a shiny
bluish black. This blue black sheen is gener-
ated by the many tiny irridescent flecks on

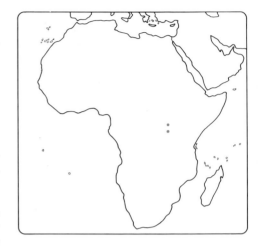

African distribution of *Ctenopoma damasi*.

Ctenopoma damasi.

the black background. At the same time the females only alter their normal colouring by the addition of a light grey longitudinal stripe.

natural habitat

The

of this species is to be found in the area around Lake Edward in East Africa. It has been found by Professor M. POLL on the Congolese side and by Dr. BERNS and Professor PETERS on the Ugandan side. *Ct. damasi* lives here in detached accumulations of water, usually heavily infested by weeds and seemingly formed as a result of flooding of the marshlands. It is also found in shallow ponds where the surface is often completely overgrown with the floating plant, *Pistia stratiotes*. It can be assumed that the temperature in these exposed ponds can rise drastically when the sun shines and must reach figures of around 34 °C, leading no doubt to a severe oxygen deficiency. In some places *Ctenopoma muriei* occurs in these waters too, illustrating its wide geographical range.

The

general care

of *Ctenopoma damasi* is not difficult. The aquarium should be set up following the guidelines for *Ct. ansorgii* or those for the next species described, *Ct. fasciolatum*. As *Ctenopoma damasi* is a relatively rare fish it is best if these fish are only kept with their own kind, with no other companion species. Alternatively, to overcome any shyness, they may share their tank with a small shoal of characins or a few platys. The males build a compact little bubble nest amongst or under floating plants, beneath which the pair spawns in the usual way. The eggs are transparent and clear and rise to the surface. The male cares for the brood alone. The larvae hatch after a day and a half approximately, at a water temperature of 18 °C and are simming around freely after a further 48 hours. Small amounts of powdered food such as Tetra MikroMin should be strewn on to the surface to tempt the fry. An aerator with a gentle bubbling action will ensure that the food is well distributed throughout the tank. If well looked after, these youngsters will soon start to grow.

The locals often prove to be hard-working and informative assistants when it comes to catching these fish.

It was in 1912 that the smallish, 8 cm long, very peaceable species

◆ Ctenopoma fasciolatum
(BOULENGER, 1899)

was imported into Germany for the first time. At the time it was an interesting novelty and parallels were drawn between it and the Asiatic paradise fish, *Macropodus opercularis*. This banded species of climbing perch is also a bubble nest builder. On reaching adulthood, the males exhibit very elongated dorsal and anal fins, in contrast to the females which do have this feature though by no means to such a pronounced extent. Other distinguishing features in the males are the bold, almost bluish black, zig zag stripes which again do not stand out so much in the females, as well as a light grey longitudinal stripe that appears along the middle of his body when he is in the mood for courting. These fish are somewhat shy but in a well-planted aquarium in the company of some other compatible fish, they become active swimmers that are fascinating to watch. *Ctenopoma fasciolatum* is not aggressive towards fish of its own kind or towards other species, even smaller ones.

African distribution of *Ctenopoma fasciolatum*.

Otherwise its general care is unproblematical.

The aquarium should have a minimum length of 70 cm. The planting scheme should include some dense clumps comprising tall-stemmed subjects like *Hygrophila polysperma*, *Hygrophila stricta*, *Limnophila aquatica* and several stems of *Heteranthera zosterifolia* set out to form little stands in

Ctenopoma fasciolatum.

the background and at the sides. In front of these to the one side a red *Nymphaea lotus* should be planted to form a nice contrast and provide cover for these smaller *Ctenopoma* species as its leaves being to unfold. In the foreground two or three groups of stones should be positioned and between these a few plants of *Cryptocoryne blassii*, interspersed with some *Microsorium pteropus*. In this case too, the bed should be made up of gravel with a grain size of between 1 and 3 mm. A few floating plants like *Pistia stratiotes* and *Riccia flutans* will round off the picture nicely. The temperature is set at 25 °C and the aquarium must be lit in the standard way for 12 hours per day. The fish should have a diet that includes sun- and freeze-dried food from the Tetra-Delica line, such as the red mosquito larvae. For a bit of variety you can also offer them flaked foods like TetraPhyll as a healthy, high-vitamin, vegetable-based supplement. For decades now *Ctenopoma fasciolatum* has often been confused with *Ctenopoma nanum*. The resultant uncertainty is still present in the minds of a number of authors and aquarists, even though the original descriptions of these two species are quite clear about their identification. In terms of its physical build *Ct. nanum* has great similarities to *Ct. ansorgii* and *Ct. damasi*. *Ctenopoma fasciolatum*, on the other hand, is at first glance recognised as being much deeper-bodied and makes a much different impression thanks to its ten to twelve vertical zig zag stripes. The distribution of *Ct. fasciolatum* extends over areas of Zaire, from the upper reaches of the River Congo near Mosembe to its estuary at Boma.

Analysis of the water in these areas gave slightly acidic values with a low mineral content. The water conditions for a breeding tank should reflect these findings. Such a tank should also contain similar groups of tall-stemmed plants growing up to the surface and a few floating plants, as recommended for general care. The temperature here should be raised to 28 °C though and the container stood in a quiet corner. Subdued lighting and a filtration system that does not cause excessive water

movement — preferably using a Brillant Filter — are also recommended. Once the aquarium has been set up in this way, it should be left to stand fully functioning for a week or a fortnight before the breeding pair — specimens 7 to 8 cm long, if possible — are put in. The breeder's patience may be severely tested before the male commences building his bubble nest. It is usually sited at the surface amongst floating plants, very loosely formed and often incorporating plant particles. In spite of a number of "phantom" matings, it might often take another four days before spawning actually takes place. With a bit of luck and patience mating will then take place under the nest, with the male entwining himself around his partner from below while she remains in the normal swimming mode. Once the eggs are released, the female leaves the scene and the eggs rise slowly to the surface. Large specimens can be very productive, with up to 1000 eggs quite common. For is it unusual for the pair to continue to spawn on several consecutive days. As the parent fish do not molest their own spawn or their young, the offspring will come to no harm. The larvae hatch about 18 hours after spawning and some two days after that, they are swimming between the plants up to the surface, looking for tiny scraps of food. Copious amounts of pulverised Tetra MikroMin are ideal. Under such conditions the little *Ctenopoma fasciolatum* will grow quickly and reach a length of ca. 1.5 cm in eight weeks or so. At this size they will be showing the zig zag stripes so typical of their parents. Unfortunately, the youngsters tend to grow at different rates and it will be advantageous to the development of the smaller ones if the "prodigies" can be moved on to another tank. So that was a portrait of *Ctenopoma fasciolatum*, a beautiful, placid and straightforward climbing perch from Africa. We can only hope that a captive breeding programme will help to promote the popularity and availability of this species.

One of the largest of all the climbing perches, said in the original description to grow up to 20 cm in length, with a distribution covering the whole of West Africa, is

▶ *Ctenopoma kingsleyae*
(GUNTHER, 1866)

which, despite its great size, has a very placid nature. Obviously, you would not recommend that it be kept in a community tank with small companions because these fish would eventually end up on the menu. However, any fish over 6 cm in length and not too slimly built can be kept with fully

Ctenopoma kingsleyae.

grown *Ctenopoma kingsleyae* without fear. These fish are not particularly colourful. The dark grey of the upper part of their body is nicely complemented by a silvery green sheen on the lower side of the body. A round, black spot on the caudal peduncle can only be regarded as a distinctive feature in younger individuals. The pectoral fins have a light yellow colour. *Ct. kingsleyae* do not care for their brood but spawn in the open water. The sexes can only be differentiated after they have reached a size of 12 cm and by using the technique described in the introduction to climbing perches.

According to the original description the
natural habitat
extends over the coastal areas of West Africa from Gambia through the Niger delta in Nigeria to Cameroon.

In the course of my own field trips to West Africa, however, I have only been able to catch these fish in Sierra Leone. Here they were particularly numerous in the clear, flowing watercourses of the Kasewe forest region.

The biggest specimens were just 15 cm long. It was easy to watch them in large numbers in a lake-like stretch of water that was very low in minerals and acidic. The temperature was 25 °C. The situation was different in the north of Sierra Leone. Here I caught this species in rice fields and the

In Africa catching fish is women's work but the ladies in question are more than willing to help out our research efforts.

associated ditches near the town of Kambia. In this biotope the water temperature was 30 °C. A noticeable feature here was the difference in the colouring between these fish and those from the Kasewe location. Whereas the specimens from the forest region showed more grey and fewer green shades, the situation was the reverse with these fish from the more open stretches of water. The latter had a predominantly green sheen covering the almost black body so that I thought at first that it was a different species. Usually it was possible to watch a number of individuals at once.

For keeping this species, large aquaria are the only feasible option. These should be

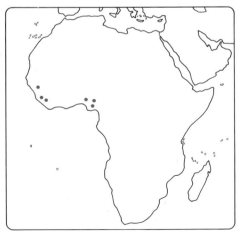

African distribution of *Ctenopoma kingsleyae*.

157

over 130 cm long by 50 cm wide and deep, at the very least. Dense clumps of plants should be provided at intervals with good open stretches of free swimming room. The temperature should be between 24 and 26 °C. For their general care and, as far as we can tell so far, for breeding, water values are of secondary importance.

For
breeding
it is essential that you make a large aquarium available. As well as dense clumps of plants in some places you should also provide some cavities or crevices in rock structures in which the female can take refuge because the males can become very aggressive towards their partners when mating time approaches.

The water surface should have a good cover of floating plants and the temperature needs to be set at 26 °C. *Ct. kingsleyae* release their spawn in the open water after a brief entanglement. The eggs then rise to the surface and develop amongst the leaves of the floating plants.

This is a very prolific species. Fully grown specimens can lay more than one thousand eggs. As the parent fish are wont to eat their own spawn, they should be removed from the breeding tank when spawning is over. The larvae hatch after 36 hours and are free swimming after another

Table No. 11

Locality:	Masene, near the town of Kambia, Sierra Leone Ditches between the rice fields
Clarity:	cloudy
Colour:	dark
pH value:	5.7
D general hardness	under 1 °dH
D carbonate hardness	under 1 °dH
Conductivity:	15 microsiemens at 30 °C
Nitrite:	0.05 mg/l
Water depth:	up to 50 cm
Water movement:	little
Water temperature:	30 °C
Date of tests:	19. 11. 1978
Time:	12.00

two days. As their first food they can be given Tetra MikroMin powdered food. At about four weeks old the black fleck on the caudal peduncle starts to form and the young fish begin taking in atmospheric air. *Ctenopoma kingsleyae* is a very interesting species of climbing perch and deserves the attention of a lot more amateur aquarists. You should just bear in mind that these fish are at their most colourful when they are still under 10 cm in length.

Ct. kingsleayae, 5 cm long, just caught in a stream in the Kasewe Forest in Sierra Leone.

A typical biotope of climbing perch is West Africa.

A rarely imported species is

♦ *Ctenopoma maculatum*
(THOMINOT, 1886)

These climbing perches, which also grow to a length of 20 cm, have unfortunately seldom been seen in our aquaria. The few specimens that I have caught myself behaved in a very retiring way in the company of other fish, one might even say rather timidly. They were generally 6 cm long. It is only when they have reached a considerably greater size that the characteristics for differentiating the sexes become visible. The spine-edged patches of scales behind the eye and near the root of the tail can only be made out when they have attained a length of 10 cm at least. The size that this species can grow to in captivity has not yet been established. The juvenile coloration of *Ct. maculata* is very attractive. At this stage they are a dark brown colour and a light yellow ring stretches from the dorsal fin around the body,

Ctenopoma maculatum.

ending between the ventral and anal fins. There is also a light yellow pattern of transverse rings from the head to back up this pattern so that the total effect brings to mind the Asiatic chocolate gouramis, *Sphaerichthys osphromenoides*. When it reaches a size of 4 to 5 cm, this colour fades and changes to a feeble greyish brown shade as its main body colour, with a bold dark spot in the middle of the body.

The
natural habitat
of this species is found in South Cameroon, Gabon and Rio Muni, where it occurs in the tributaries of the Dja, Ntem and Ogowe river systems. However, I was only able to catch odd specimens of this species and intermittently at that. They lead a very retiring existence, concealed in the densely overgrown bank zones of little streams with flowing, very soft, clean water. The water level often stood at only 20 cm. Details are given in Table 9.

The Kribi river, since renamed as the Kienke river and given in the original description as a site for these fish, did not yield any of them when I attempted to confirm their existence there.

For the
general care
of this species, one should follow the guidelines given for the species *Ct. acutirostre*, *Ct. ocellatum* and *Ct. oxyrhynchum*. The tank should not be too small. Additions of a flaked food such as TetraMin are advisable as this food helps to ensure a balanced vitamin intake. The water temperature should be around 25 to 27 °C. Dense clumps of plants are required in some places as these fish become very timid in their absence. This species is not aggressive and is suited to a community tank containing almost any other larger species. If they are to have optimum conditions the only form of tank that can be considered is the "large aquarium for labyrinth fish".

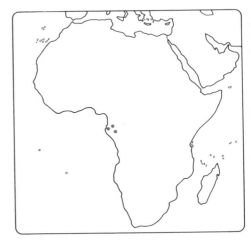

African distribution of *Ctenopoma maculatum*.

A natural habitat of *Ctenopoma maculatum* in South Cameroon.

Another species that grows to a relatively large size is

◆ *Ctenopoma multispinis*
(PETERS, 1844)

This species can attain a length of 15 cm and is a fast and agile swimmer. Whereas other species of *Ctenopoma* often spend much of their time motionless, *Ct. multispinis* is constantly on the move. This fish should only be kept in the company of other species that are large enough to take care of themselves, because they are greedy and sometimes aggressive creatures. An ideal companion for them would be the Asiatic climbing fish, *Anabas testudineus*, as both species have similar behaviour patterns.

Ctenopoma multispinis is also capable of leaving the water and will migrate overland to other stretches of water when the

Ctenopoma multispinis.

weather is particularly damp. It seems that the only way of distinguishing the sexes is by the patches of spiny scales. They are free spawners and release their eggs into the open water after their usual brief courtship ritual. The eggs develop without any after-care on the part of the parents.

Their
natural habitat

extends over a vast area of south eastern Africa, including the major rivers there, their tributaries and associated swampland in southern Zaire, Mozambique, Zambia, Zimbabwe and Botswana. The specimen shown here was caught in Mozambique by D. SCHALLER from Munich who kindly lent me this and others for observation.

Ct. multispinis is best kept in a large aquarium. This is not absolutely essential but encourages the fish to develop and behave more naturally. If possible a number of individuals of this species should be kept together with some equally sized, robust specimens of other species so that any outbursts of aggravation can be shared out amongst them.

For their diet they must be given earthworms, mosquito and other insect larvae, young mealworms, shrimps, young fish up to 1.5 cm in length and other high-protein food. Once or twice a week they should also be offered high-vitamin flaked food in the form of large flakes like Tetra Marin and food tablets such as TabiMin. The aquarium must be well covered as these fish can jump well and can propel themselves through the smallest target. If properly treated, these fish become very confiding and it is not unusual for them to jump out of the water towards their keeper when he removes the cover to feed them.

The water temperature can be between 25 and 27 °C. For preference the plants should be of a tough, robust constitution such as the *Anubias* group from West Africa. A couple of hideouts for their few moments of rest might also be appreciated. A partial surface cover of floating plants, including some *Pistia stratiotes*, would probably also give them a greater sense of security. Water quality values seem to be of lesser importance. A powerful filtration system is advantageous for the wellbeing of these fish and a partial water change (one quarter to one third of the contents every fortnight to three weeks) should be carried out as a matter of course. *Ct. multispinis* is a very interesting species that constitutes a charming subject for study for research aquarists and nature lovers alike.

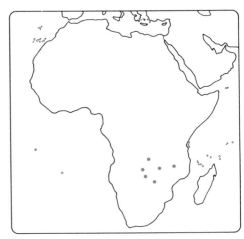

African distribution of *Ctenopoma multispinis*.

A species of climbing perch that has only recently been brought back to Europe by Dr. PETERS and Dr. BERNS is

▶ **Ctenopoma muriei**
(BOULENGER, 1906)

This species generally grows to 8 cm in length. The sexes cannot be differentiated on the grounds of any differences in colour. The only possibility is the more distinctive patches of spiny scales behind the eyes and on the caudal peduncle in the males. On

Ctenopoma muriei.

163

reaching full adulthood the females may be rather bigger.

The
natural habitat
of these fish is from north east to east Africa, from the White Nile near Khartoum to the area around Lake Albert, Lake Kyoga, Lake Victoria and Lake Edward. Its southern limit is the north of Lake Tanganyika and to the west, the Chad basin and the neighbouring basin of the Mayo Kebi. With this wide distribution, there are some morphological distinctions that can be made. They are found in small, shallow accumulations of water, the marshes and flooded areas around rivers and in little pools, especially in "weed-infested" parts. These waters are often very low in oxygen and become heated to temperatures around 34 °C. Investigations revealed that they only live in these shallow, warm conditions for short periods, generally preferring deeper, cool stretches of water. *Ct. muriei* are lively swimmers. In the aquarium they like to patrol the middle water zone and some consideration should be given to this preference when setting up the tank decoration. As well as a dense planting scheme for the rear of the tank and a number of cave structures and bogwood pieces, you should also allow plenty of free swimming room. The water temperature can be around 25 °C and a powerful motor filter should be provided to ensure a light water movement. A partial cover of floating plants like *Pistia stratiotes*, the water lettuce, or *Ceratopteris pteridoides*, will make this species feel more secure and allow it to be seen to best advantage. The "large aquarium for labyrinth fish" is the version that will best suit *Ct. muriei*.

Currently available reports tell us that breeding this species is not difficult. The breeding tank should not be too small, lengths in excess of 100 cm being advisable. The water temperature should be raised to 28 °C. One female seems to do well when accompanied by two or three males.

Ct. muriei are free spawners and usually perform their courtship ritual in the evening twilight. After a number of chases, with the males pursuing the female, one of the former will attempt to entwine with her during a break in the swimming. He releases her from his embrace after about three seconds and the eggs float up to the surface. This species does not look after its brood. Over 1000 eggs may be laid. The larvae hatch after about 25 hours.

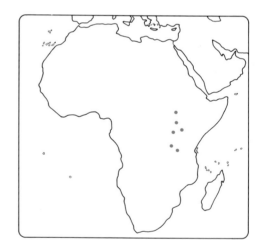

African distribution of *Ctenopoma muriei*.

A species that does not grow to any great size and which is easy to keep is

▶ Ctenopoma nanum
(GUNTHER, 1896)
the dwarf climbing perch.

Its full adult length is only 7 cm at most. In larger specimens sexual differentiation is quite easy. The males have a darker body colour, often ranging from dark grey to a bluish black. Compared with the females, the dorsal and anal fins are rather more pointed and are bordered with a light blue hem. The overall colour of the females is lighter and they usually exhibit a light grey, broad longitudinal stripe that extends from the middle of the body to the root of the tail. Depending on their mood, from seven to ten dark-coloured cross stripes become visible in both sexes, these being holder in the females during their courtship display.

For some unaccountable reason, *Ct. nanum* has often been confused with *Ctenopoma fasciolatum*. *Ctenopoma nanum* is easily distinguished from *Ct. fasciolatum* in that it is smaller, does not have such a deep body, and gives a general impression of being much slimmer.

As its body pattern is simply made up of transverse stripes without any zig zag markings and as the males do not possess the elongated dorsal and anal fins — which invite comparison with the Asiatic paradise fish, *Macropodus opercularis opercularis* — it is quite simple to tell the two species apart.

Ctenopoma nanum.

African distribution of *Ctenopoma nanum*.

The
natural habitat

of *Ct. nanum* extends from south Cameroon, through Gabon and Rio Muni and
from there to the lower Congo area and into
Congo-Brazzaville. I have frequently caught
this species over the past few years in the
south eastern tributaries of the Kienke river
and in branches of the Ntem and Dja rivers
in south Cameroon. The species was also to
be found in parts of the Ogowe river system
that reaches into this area. The specimens
from the Dja tributaries appeared to me to
be somewhat more reddish brown in colour
so that at first glance you were tempted to
draw parallels with the species *Ctenopoma
brunneum* (AHL, 1927) which lives in this
area, according to the original description.
Ct. nanum lives in waterways that are often
only 3 meters wide and generally only 50 cm
deep — in fact, the upper reaches of the
major river systems. Their favourite haunts
are to overgrown bank margins and the
adjacent flooded lowlands. These fish are
also found amongst fallen leaves and in
cavities amongst eroded bank zones with
exposed tree roots. Rather more infrequently, they are also to be found in tiny
little rivulets, scarcely worthy of the name
"stream", often totally overgrown but nevertheless containing flowing water. The water
in all these locations was always very soft,

acidic and almost always flowing. In almost
every case, these waters were rarely subjected to the full force of the sun's rays and
had a temperature close to 25 °C, irrespective of the time of the year and rarely
exceeding this figure by 1 to 2 °C even in the
shade-free areas.

Ct. nanum is easy to keep and not at all
fussy. Nevertheless, there are a number of
points to bear in mind when setting up their
aquarium. Even though this fish does not
grow to a great size, you should still give it a
fairly spacious aquarium, with a minimum
size of 70 cm long by 40 cm wide and 30 cm
deep. It will certainly enjoy any densely
planted clumps with tall-stemmed plants
reaching up to the surface, such as *Cabomba
aquatica*, *Cabomba carolina*, the Carolinian
fanwort, or *Ceratopteris thalictroides*, the
Indian fern. Nor should you omit some decorative bogwood, planted up with a few
bushy *Microsorium pteropus* or the aquatic
fern from tropical Africa, *Bolbitis heudelotii*. A number of crevices in stony structures
will complete the picture nicely. The bed
should consist of fine gravel with a grain size
between 1 to 3 mm in diameter. Some surface cover should be provided in the form of
Riccia flutans and *Ceratopteris pteridoides*.

A Brillant Filter will ensure clean, clear
water and provide the requisite gentle water
movement. The temperature should be set at

Table No. 12

Locality:	near Akom, between the towns of Kribi and Ebolowa
Clarity:	clear
Colour:	brown
pH value:	5.6
D general hardness	under 1 °dH
D carbonate hardness	under 1 °dH
Conductivity:	6 microsiemens at 24.5 °C
Nitrite:	0.00 mg/l
Water depth:	up to 50 cm
Water movement:	flowing
Water temperature:	24.5 °C
Date of tests:	16. 3. 1977
Time:	16.30

to that found in their natural biotope. The larvae hatch after about 24 hours and the fry are swimming freely after a further 70 hours. At this point the parents should be taken out of the breeding tank. As a first food, I recommend a pulverised flaked food like Tetra MikroMin, crushed between the fingers. A slow-running, fine aerator will ensure that the food is well distributed throughout the tank. A few days later you should supplement this regime with the growth-promoting flaked food TetraOvim which should then take over as their exclusive diet after a further five days. A partial water change after two weeks, repeated at three to five day intervals, will ensure clean, healthy water and encourage the growth of the fry. Under such conditions the little *Ctenopoma nanum* will rapidly develop into fine specimens.

24 to 25 °C and the aquarium can be lit at the normal rate of 0.5 Watts per liter. These recommendations apply to a single species aquarium. However, if you want to have a community tank, you should follow the guidelines given for the "little aquarium for labyrinth fish".

For

breeding

this species, you should set up the tank and then transfer to it a pair that are sexually mature and, if possible, that have demonstrated their readiness to mate in the main tank. The male will soon build a little bubble nest. After an ardent courtship the female will be tempted under the nest where she will lay her eggs for subsequent fertilization by her mate. These then float up into the bubble nest and, once egg laying is completed, will be looked after and defended by the male alone until the fry are swimming freely around. It is a prolific species and healthy specimens can produce 600 to 800 eggs. If they are to breed successfully, they require soft, acidic water, as close as possible

Many *Anubia* have an emergent growth habit in the watercourses in Cameroon.

One of the larger species of climbing perch is

▶ *Ctenopoma ocellatum*
(PELLEGRIN, 1899)

This species has already been given a number of common names, including the leopard climbing perch, the eyespot (ocellus) climbing perch and the cross-striped climbing perch. The first of these arose because it was frequently confused with *Ct. acutirostre*, which is very similar to it in body shape. Generally speaking, *Ct. acuti-*

Ctenopoma ocellatum.

rostre grows to 12 to 15 cm under aquarium conditions. However, the literature records lengths of up to 30 cm, though these must be regarded as quite exceptional. Unfortunately, this species has only rarely been imported so we have very few reports based on personal experience. Usually, the specimens on sale at dealers are in the 5 cm size range. Sexual differentiation is only possible in larger examples. As this species appears to be a free spawner whose eggs develop without any brood care from either parent, here too the only distinguishing features are the patches of spiny scales behind the eyes and at the root of the tail. No distinguishable difference in colour or in the shape of the fins has as yet been identified.

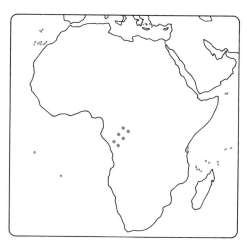

African distribution of *Ctenopoma ocellatum*.

The
natural habitat

is the Congo river system in Zaire. This also includes the areas around Stanley Pool, near the towns of Kinshasa and Brazzaville and as far as the Stanley Falls, as well as parts of the fast flowing and the calmer zones of the River Congo with its countless tributaries. They often live in association with *Ct. acutirostre* and a more detailed description of the biotopes in question is given under the section on that species. *Ct. ocellatum* is a crepuscular fish. They often stand almost motionless in the water. With just their pectoral fins working away like tiny oars, the fish drift through the water like a leaf, constantly on the lookout for something to eat. It is a totally harmless fish and shows no aggression at all towards other species. Even so, you should be careful not to keep them with small fish that would fit nicely into their mouths. They might just be tempted and any bite-sized fish would vanish into their cavernous mouths in a flash!

The
general care

of these fish is quite straightforward. Their tanks should have lots of densely planted zones together with some hideouts amongst rocks and roots. It is not advisable to keep them in association with very fast swimming species of other genera because *Ct. ocellatum* will react by withdrawing to the cover of the plants and scarcely ever be seen. However, it does need companion fish and once it settles down, becomes quite confiding. Its aquarium should not be too small and the "large aquarium for labyrinth fish" should be regarded as the ideal. The water quality values are of secondary importance, but, if possible, should be somewhere in the soft, slightly acidic range. The water temperature should be set between 25 and 27 °C. A gentle water movement is advisable because these fish like to sit in the current or let themselves be carried along in it. Large-flaked food like Tetra Marin or broken food tablets such as Tetra TabiMin or TetraTips FD should be fed to them on a continuous rota. A regular water change is recommended, say, every two to three weeks and involving a quarter to a third of the contents to guarantee vitality and healthy growth in your *Ct. ocellatum*. Unfortunately, nothing is known about any successful breeding attempts.

After quite a long interval, Heiko BLEHER managed in 1986 to import the climbing perch known as

◗ *Ctenopoma pellegrinii*
(BOULENGER, 1902)

These slim African labyrinth fish, which are said to grow to a total length of some 10 cm, are thought to be free spawners. The characteristic features of this species are 13 to 15 transverse stripes and a dark speck on the caudal peduncle that usually runs lengthwise into the root of the tail. These fish are considered to be placid and fit in readily with any other species, provided these are not too small. They are lively swimmers, particularly when on the lookout for scraps of food. The location in which the examples described originally were found lies 10 km south of Kindu in Zaire. BLEHER also caught the specimens that he imported near to this locality. The fish were living in a small stream on the Lualaba which flows from the south into the Zaire. Here the water values for general and carbonate hardness were a little over 1° dH, with an

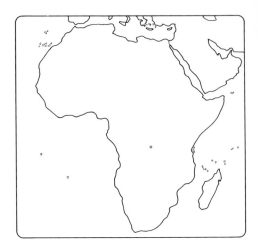

African distribution of *Ctenopoma pellegrinii*.

electrical conductivity of 65—75 microsiemens at 29°C water temperature and a dH of 4.8. The fish live in very soft, acidic waters.

Hitherto they have proved to be straightforward aquarium subjects in medium hard to hard water. As yet nothing is known about their reproductive biology.

Ctenopoma pellegrinii.

Another very small species that was imported by Heiko BLEHER in 1986 and shows a great number of similarities to *Ctenopoma nanum* though it has not yet been properly described scientifically is

◆ *Ctenopoma spec. affin. ctenotis*

Whereas the species *Ctenopoma nanum* has a predominantly grey to brown body colour, this possibly new species looks mainly light brown to ochre yellow. Its body stripes are also quite differently patterned. They are undoubtedly bubble nest builders. As far as we can tell, *Ctenopoma spec. affin. nanum* reaches a total length of 6 to 7 cm. The species was caught in a biotope that it shared with *Ctenopoma pellegrinii* near Kindu in Zaire. The fish were living in a small stream on the Lualaba which flows from the south into the Zaire. Here the water values for general and carbonate hardness were a little over 1° dH, with an electrical conductivity of 65−75 microsiemens at 29°C water temperature and a pH of 4.8. Several speci-

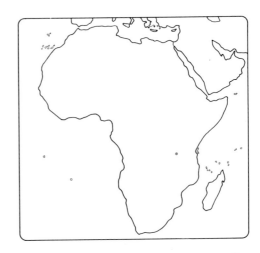

African distribution of *Ctenopoma spec. affin. ctenotis*.

mens of this species have been imported but, unfortunately, they have not yet bred in captivity. It is possible that the fish is indeed *Ctenopoma ctenotis* (BOULENGER, 1920) which had not been imported live before 1986.

Ctenopoma spec. affin. ctenotis.

As a result of a decision by the Nomenclature Commission in 1989, *Ctenopoma oxyrhynchum* has reverted to the name of

◆ *Ctenopoma weeksii*
(BOULENGER, 1896)

This species grows up to 10 cm long and of late has been one of the climbing perches most frequently encountered in the amateur aquarium. Sexual differentiation is not possible by comparison of any differences in coloration or fin structure but only by the

Ctenopoma weeksii.

172

presence of more highly developed patches of spiny scales behind the eye and on the caudal peduncle of the male.

The
natural habitat
is given in the original description as the Yembe River and the Ubangi area in Zaire. It seems that no further information on the biotope, including water values and temperatures, is available. In the aquarium the care of these fish is quite straightforward. It does not have any special requirements and fits in easily with all other species of fish, provided they are not too small. Its appearance reminds one immediately of the related species *Ct. acutirostre* and *Ct. ocellatum* but its behaviour is generally much more vital. These fish should not be kept in too small an aquarium and a size of 70 cm long by 40 cm wide and 30 cm deep should be regarded as the minimum dimensions. Dense clumps of plants in parts and some hideouts in the form of holes in roots and rocky structures are advisable. As material for the bed you should use gravel with a grain size between 1 and 3 mm. A few floating plants will help screen the fish and give them a feeling of security. Good water filtration with a gentle water movement is recommended, preferably using a Tetra Brillant Filter as a high performance filter with a grooved cartridge and filter chamber. To enhance the performance in a larger aquarium, a second grooved cartridge should be provided. The water temperature should be about 25 °C and the everyday aquarium should be lit at the standard rate of 0.5 Watts per liter.

Breeding
this fish does not seem to be all that difficult and has often been accomplished in the last few years. Presumably, all the fish of this species that are currently sold through dealers are captive bred, so that wild stocks are not endangered. For breeding purposes you should select a fairly mature pair. Experience has shown that fish around two years old are best. A tank that is set up in the same

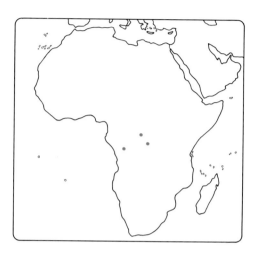

African distribution of *Ctenopoma weeksii*.

way as for their general care is equally suitable for breeding. The females should be ready to spawn and have a full, rounded girth. These fish dispense with any nest building and spawn after a courtship that takes place near the tank bottom. The eggs then rise to the surface and attach themselves to plants. The parents do not care for their brood at all and should be removed from the tank once spawning is concluded. As with all other species of labyrinth fish, you should exercise a good deal of care when handling them in a net because they are likely to get caught up in the net material and injure themselves, sometimes quite seriously. For this reason it is advisable to catch them by hand or with a catching jar. The larvae hatch after about 24 hours and the young fish are free swimming after a further 70 hours. The number of offspring can be very high and 700 to 900 fry is not unusual. For the eggs and fry to develop well, soft, slightly acidic water with a low mineral content is recommended. The youngsters are not difficult to raise and a full description has already been given under *Ct. nanum*.

Summary

This description of the individual species concludes this presentation of the labyrinth fish and the recommendations for their care. I have tried to cover all the species that have been imported live to Germany and which are available through dealers, and to illustrate each of them with photographs. I cannot claim that this presentation is complete from the systematic standpoint. I have gone to great pains to catch many species myself in Africa and Asia and to bring them back to Germany so that they are available in our aquaria now. Various quite rare species have now acquired modest popularity as a result of successful breeding. But another purpose behind this book was to provide encouragement to any interested beginners in the aquarist hobby and, possibly, stimulate "old hands" to perhaps rethink some of their old ideas. But if just one or two more people would consider these fish as subjects for their own aquarium, then I shall consider my aim fulfilled, because they are some of the most beautiful and interesting of all ornamental fish.

Let us hope that this book can lead to a broadening of the interest in these magnificently coloured and remarkable fish in the same way that the founding of the International Society did in 1979.

The Autor

Horst Linke, born in 1938, and a trained sound technician, has had an enthusiastic interest in aquaria since his early youth. And right from the start it was fighting fish and other labyrinth fish that formed the focal point of his attentions.

In 1963 he took advantage of a trip to the "Dark Continent" to acquaint himself with the natural habitat of the African labyrinth fish. It was at this point that he began to develop a second side to his hobby, namely breeding, as well as a careful study of the biotopes of West African cichlids. Since 1973 he has made many field trips to Cameroon, Nigeria, Togo, Ghana, Sierra Leone, Kenya and Tanzania, as well as to Asian countries like Sri Lanka, Thailand, Malaysia, Hong Kong, Bangladesh, Borneo and Sumatra. In the course of the expeditions he undertook research into the natural habitats of labyrinth fish which had some interesting implications for their care in captivity and gave him the opportunity to import some new species to Germany. He has published many articles in specialist aquarium magazines and journals, giving detailed accounts of his travels vividly illustrated with his own photographs of fish and habitats. His contacts with various museums and universities have meant that many of his findings have been thoroughly evaluated and accepted at the highest level.

Horst Linke has been actively involved in the aquarist hobby for many years now. His interest still centres on the labyrinth fish and the group of West African cichlids and he is frequently invited to give lectures to societies and conferences. He still believes that the exchange of views and experiences is one of the essential aspects of our hobby.